Study Guide to
The American Psychiatric Press
Textbook of
Consultation-Liaison Psychiatry

Study Guide to The American Psychiatric Press Textbook of Consultation-Liaison Psychiatry

Jude Berman, Ed.D.,
James R. Rundell, M.D., and
Michael G. Wise, M.D.

American Psychiatric Press, Inc.

Washington, DC
London, England

Copyright © 1999 American Psychiatric Press, Inc.
ALL RIGHTS RESERVED
Manufactured in the United States of America on acid-free paper
02   01   00   99   4   3   2   1

American Psychiatric Press, Inc.
1400 K Street, N.W.
Washington, DC   20005
www.appi.org

First Edition

Library of Congress Cataloging-in-Publication Data
Berman, Judith, 1950–
    Study guide to the American Psychiatric Press textbook of
    consultation-liaison psychiatry / Judith Berman, James R. Rundell,
    and Michael G. Wise. — 1st ed.
        p.   cm.
    Includes bibliographical references and index.
    ISBN 0-88048-805-0
    1. Consultation-liaison psychiatry.   2. Consultation-liaison
    psychiatry—Examinations, questions, etc.   I. Rundell, James R.,
    1957–   .   II. Wise, Michael G., 1944–   .   III. American
    Psychiatric Press.   IV. American Psychiatric Press textbook of
    consultation-liaison psychiatry.   V. Title.
    RC455.2.C65E87   1999 Suppl.
    616.89′0076—dc21
    DNLM/DLC
    for Library of Congress   98-53143
                                                                              CIP

British Library Cataloguing in Publication Data
A CIP record is available from the British Library.

About the Authors

Jude Berman, Ed.D., is a professional educator, writer, and developmental editor based in Emeryville, California.

James R. Rundell, M.D., is Chief of Medical Staff, Medical Group, at Ramstein Air Force Base in Germany and Associate Professor of Psychiatry at the Uniformed Services University of the Health Sciences in Bethesda, Maryland.

Michael G. Wise, M.D., is Professor and Vice-Chair at the University of California Davis Medical School, Medical Director at the Sacramento County Mental Health Treatment Center, and Director of the Consultation-Liaison Fellowship Program.

Contents

Section I
General Principles

Section II
Psychiatric Disorders in General Hospital Patients

Section III
Clinical Consultation-Liaison Settings

Section IV
Treatment

Preface

The purpose of the *Study Guide to The American Psychiatric Press Textbook of Consultation-Liaison Psychiatry* is to provide readers of *The American Psychiatric Press Textbook of Consultation-Liaison Psychiatry* with an opportunity to evaluate their knowledge of the material contained in that textbook.

The American Psychiatric Press Textbook of Consultation-Liaison Psychiatry is a clinically focused, comprehensive textbook that contains 44 chapters (1171 pages) about the practice of consultation-liaison psychiatry. We do not anticipate that readers will read the *Textbook* cover to cover, but rather will read individual chapters of particular interest or clinical relevance. With that in mind, the *Study Guide* contains questions for each chapter. This allows the reader to test his or her understanding of the material by answering questions and further broadening knowledge by checking the correctness of the answers. Answers to all questions, along with the corresponding reference page(s) in the *Textbook,* are conveniently located at the end of each chapter in the *Study Guide.*

The 44 chapters in the *Study Guide* correspond directly to the chapters in the *Textbook;* however, readers of the *Essentials of Consultation-Liaison Psychiatry,* a synopsis of the *The American Psychiatric Press Textbook of Consultation-Liaison Psychiatry,* may also find the *Study Guide* useful. *Essentials of Consultation-Liaison Psychiatry* contains the 34 most clinically relevant chapters from the *Textbook* and presents these chapters in a condensed manner that facilitates learning and applications of concepts to patient care. Each chapter in the *Study Guide* contains a footnote indicating the corresponding chapter in the *Essentials of Consultation-Liaison Psychiatry.*

The *Study Guide, Textbook,* and *Essentials* were designed for fellows, residents, and clinicians to assess and strengthen their knowledge about the practice of psychiatry in patients with other medical illnesses. In addition, use of this *Study Guide* will provide an enhanced knowledge base for subspecialty examinations (e.g., General Psychiatry Board Examinations, added qualifications in Geriatric

Psychiatry), state licensing examinations, and national certifying examinations.

Dr. Jude Berman took the lead in developing this *Study Guide*. Dr. Berman is highly skilled and experienced in the process of developing examinations and has impressive credentials in the editing and production of textbooks. We (James R. Rundell and Michael G. Wise) helped refine the questions in the *Study Guide* to ensure relevance to practicing clinicians.

In summary, we believe you will find the *Study Guide to The American Psychiatric Press Textbook of Consultation-Liaison Psychiatry* an important addition to your continuing medical education and clinical practice. We also welcome your feedback so that we can improve future editions.

James R. Rundell, M.D.
Michael G. Wise, M.D.

Section I
General Principles

Chapter 1

History of Consultation-Liaison Psychiatry

 QUESTIONS

Directions: Select the single best response for each of the following questions:

1.1 Who of the following was a pioneering psychobiologist?
   A. Benjamin Rush.
   B. Adolf Meyers.
   C. Edward Billings.
   D. George W. Henry.
   E. John Romano.

1.2 According to Lipowski, in consultation-liaison psychiatry, the term *liaison* refers to
   A. The psychiatrist-patient relationship.
   B. Contact between teaching physicians and medical students, residents, and fellows.
   C. Integration between medicine and psychiatry.
   D. Clinical service contact with nonpsychiatrist physicians.
   E. All of the above.

1.3 Consultation-liaison psychiatry experienced its most rapid growth during the period circa
   A. 1900–1915.
   B. 1920–1935.
   C. 1935–1960.
   D. 1960–1975.
   E. 1975–1980s.

No corresponding chapter appears in the *Essentials of Consultation-Liaison Psychiatry*.

1.4   Which of the following accounted for the rapid growth of consultation-liaison services?
   A.   NIMH support of consultation-liaison services.
   B.   Rapid growth of psychiatry following World War I.
   C.   Rapid growth of psychiatry following World War II.
   D.   Rapid growth in general medicine.
   E.   Development of dual psychiatry/primary care training programs.

1.5   Among Lipowski's five models of consultation, the situation model
   A.   Is concerned with the interaction between the patient and the clinical team.
   B.   Involves the patient as a central figure in an operational group that includes the patient, clinical staff, other patients, and patient's family.
   C.   Is focused on the consultee's problem with a given patient.
   D.   Is crisis-oriented.
   E.   Involves a rapid assessment of the patient's problems and coping style, as well as incisive therapeutic intervention by the consultant.

1.6   Which of the following is false?
   A.   Billings was the first writer to use the term *liaison psychiatry.*
   B.   About one-third of medical patients referred for psychiatric consultation are 65 years and older.
   C.   The first Consultation-Liaison Research Forum took place in 1990.
   D.   All of the above.
   E.   None of the above.

Directions: For each of the statements below, one or more of the answers is correct. Choose

   A.   If 1, 2, and 3 are correct.
   B.   If only 1 and 3 are correct.
   C.   If only 2 and 4 are correct.
   D.   If only 4 is correct.
   E.   If all are correct.

1.7   Among the chief features of the organizational phase of consultation-liaison psychiatry are
   1.   Growth of relevant literature.
   2.   Evaluation of consultation-liaison activities.
   3.   Expansion of research activities.
   4.   Expansion of teaching activities.

ANSWERS*

1.1 The answer is **B.** Adolf Meyers was a pioneering psychobiologist. **(p. 4)**

1.2 The answer is **D.** According to Lipowski, in consultation-liaison psychiatry, the term *liaison* refers to clinical service contact with nonpsychiatrist physicians. **(p. 4)**

1.3 The answer is **E.** Consultation-liaison psychiatry experienced its most rapid growth during the period circa 1975–1980s. **(p. 7)**

1.4 The answer is **A.** Rapid growth resulted from the NIMH decision to support the development and expansion of consultation-liaison services throughout the United States. **(p. 7)**

1.5 The answer is **A.** Among Lipowski's five models of consultation, the situation model is concerned with the interaction between the patient and the clinical team. **(p. 6)**

1.6 The answer is **E.** All of the statements are true: Billings was the first writer to use the term *liaison psychiatry*. About one-third of medical patients referred for psychiatric consultation are 65 years and older. The first Consultation-Liaison Research Forum took place in 1990. **(pp. 5–7)**

1.7 The answer is **C.** Chief features of the organizational phase of consultation-liaison psychiatry include evaluation of consultation-liaison activities and expansion of teaching activities. **(p. 5)**

---

*Page numbers within answer sections refer to *The American Psychiatric Press Textbook of Consultation-Liaison Psychiatry.*

Chapter 2

The Process of Consultation and Organization of a Consultation-Liaison Psychiatry Service

QUESTIONS

Directions: Select the single best response for each of the following questions:

2.1 Basic knowledge for performing consultation and liaison activities includes an understanding of all of the following **EXCEPT**
   A. Neurosurgery.
   B. Psychotherapy.
   C. Geriatrics.
   D. Forensics issues.
   E. Psychiatric differential diagnosis.

2.2 For all physicians, the most important aspect of the psychiatric consultation is
   A. Differential diagnosis.
   B. Dealing with patient disposition problems.
   C. Complete mental status examination.
   D. Patient education.
   E. Follow-up with family members.

No corresponding chapter appears in the *Essentials of Consultation-Liaison Psychiatry.*

2.3   Consultants should generally follow up patients until they are discharged
       because
       A.   Patients with neuropsychiatric signs and symptoms are at risk for
            recurrence.
       B.   Follow-up instills confidence in the medical-surgical team.
       C.   A premature sign-off is frequently related to transference or coun-
            tertransference issues.
       D.   All of the above.
       E.   None of the above.

Directions: For each of the statements below, one or more of the answers is
correct. Choose

       A.   If 1, 2, and 3 are correct.
       B.   If only 1 and 3 are correct.
       C.   If only 2 and 4 are correct.
       D.   If only 4 is correct.
       E.   If all are correct.

2.4   An initial consultation note should include
       1.   Current medications.
       2.   Impression.
       3.   Recommendations.
       4.   Psychiatric history.

2.5   If a consultant writes an order for diagnostic tests or medication with the
       sanction of a patient's attending physician, that consultant
       1.   Is free from liability.
       2.   Has violated hospital policy.
       3.   Has increased patient compliance.
       4.   Must ensure that the order is not medically contraindicated.

ANSWERS*

2.1   The answer is **A.** Basic knowledge for performing consultation and liaison
       activities does not include an understanding of neurosurgery. **(p. 13)**

---

*Page numbers within answer sections refer to *The American Psychiatric Press Textbook
of Consultation-Liaison Psychiatry.*

2.2   The answer is **B.** For all physicians, the most important aspect of the psychiatric consultation is dealing with patient disposition problems. **(p. 14)**

2.3   The answer is **D.** Consultants should generally follow up patients until they are discharged because patients with neuropsychiatric signs and symptoms are at risk for recurrence; follow-up instills confidence in the medical-surgical team; and a premature sign-off on the patient may be related to transference. **(p. 17)**

2.4   The answer is **E.** An initial consultation note should include current medications, impression, recommendations, and psychiatric history. **(p. 16)**

2.5   The answer is **D.** If a consultant writes an order for diagnostic tests or medication with the sanction of a patient's attending physician, that consultant must ensure that the order is not medically contraindicated. **(p. 17)**

Chapter 3

Economic Issues in Consultation-Liaison Psychiatry

Directions: Select the single best response for each of the following questions:

3.1 Medical patients with severe anxiety show most marked and rapid improvement when
   A. Treated with psychotherapy only.
   B. Treated with neuroleptics.
   C. Hospitalized long-term.
   D. Discharged immediately.
   E. Transferred to a psychiatric service.

3.2 Unless psychiatric comorbidity is diagnosed and treated early, general hospital patients
   A. Incur greater medical costs.
   B. Are hospitalized longer.
   C. Are exposed to more diagnostic procedures.
   D. All of the above.
   E. None of the above.

No corresponding chapter appears in the *Essentials of Consultation-Liaison Psychiatry*.

Directions: For each of the statements below, one or more of the answers is correct. Choose

> A.   If 1, 2, and 3 are correct.
> B.   If only 1 and 3 are correct.
> C.   If only 2 and 4 are correct.
> D.   If only 4 is correct.
> E.   If all are correct.

3.3   Length of hospital stay is positively correlated with
> 1.   Depression.
> 2.   Organicity.
> 3.   Anxiety.
> 4.   Elective admission.

3.4   Administering screening tests to elderly patients upon hospital admission results in
> 1.   Less surgery.
> 2.   Better psychiatric care.
> 3.   Increased costs.
> 4.   Earlier discharge.

3.5   A consultation-liaison service is most likely to be cost-effective if
> 1.   Administrative personnel are located elsewhere.
> 2.   Nonmedical personnel perform consultations.
> 3.   Medical information systems are decentralized.
> 4.   Control of billing functions is centralized.

◼ ANSWERS[*]

3.1   The answer is **B.** Medical patients with severe anxiety show most marked and rapid improvement when treated with neuroleptics. **(p. 26)**

3.2   The answer is **D.** Unless psychiatric comorbidity is diagnosed and treated early, general hospital patients incur greater medical costs, are hospitalized longer, and are exposed to more diagnostic procedures. **(p. 27)**

---

[*]Page numbers within answer sections refer to *The American Psychiatric Press Textbook of Consultation-Liaison Psychiatry.*

3.3 The answer is **A.** Length of hospital stay is positively correlated with depression, organicity, and anxiety. **(p. 25)**

3.4 The answer is **C.** Administering screening tests to elderly patients upon hospital admission results in better psychiatric care and earlier discharge. **(p. 26)**

3.5 The answer is **D.** A consultation-liaison service is most likely to be cost-effective if control of billing functions is centralized. **(p. 35)**

Chapter 4

Liaison Psychiatry

QUESTIONS

Directions: Select the single best response for each of the following questions:

4.1 Most studies of inpatient medical populations are flawed because of
   A. Measurement problems.
   B. Failure to consider the seriousness of the medical illness.
   C. Lack of randomization of control and experimental subjects.
   D. All of the above.
   E. None of the above.

4.2 Cognitive impairment detected during hospitalization predicts nursing home placement
   A. Within 2 months of discharge.
   B. Within 3 months of discharge.
   C. Within 4 months of discharge.
   D. Within 5 months of discharge.
   E. Within 6 months of discharge.

4.3 Compared with traditional consultation, liaison psychiatry interventions are more likely to
   A. Detect significant DSM-III-R psychiatric morbidity.
   B. Result in nursing home placement at discharge.
   C. Increase length of hospital stay.
   D. Increase rehospitalizations.
   E. Increase rehabilitation days.

This chapter also corresponds to Chapter 1 in the *Essentials of Consultation-Liaison Psychiatry.*

4.4   A model of psychiatric training for primary care physicians that is based on the case method is called
A. Consultation model.
B. Liaison model.
C. Bridge model.
D. Hybrid model.
E. Autonomous, psychiatric model.

4.5   Forestalling the recurrence of psychiatric or psychological symptoms is accomplished by
A. Primary prevention.
B. Secondary prevention.
C. Tertiary prevention.
D. Quaternary prevention.
E. None of the above.

4.6   Which of the following is true?
A. Consultation psychiatry is primarily a secondary prevention effort.
B. The milieu model of liaison psychiatry relies more on hospital governance than on triage.
C. Prepaid care is associated with increased detection of and psychosocial counseling for depression in patients.
D. All of the above.
E. None of the above.

Directions: For each of the statements below, one or more of the answers is correct. Choose

A. If 1, 2, and 3 are correct.
B. If only 1 and 3 are correct.
C. If only 2 and 4 are correct.
D. If only 4 is correct.
E. If all are correct.

4.7   Psychiatric clearance is now standard for
1. All high-risk obstetrics/gynecology patients.
2. Patients with repeated hospital admissions.
3. Patients with diagnostic problems.
4. Drug overdose patients in the intensive care unit.

4.8 To improve health care and control costs, the practice guidelines formulated by the Agency for Health Care Policy and Research focus on
1. Expanded use of the consultation model.
2. Further development of liaison psychiatry.
3. Developing autonomy in nonpsychiatric staff.
4. Assisting patients and practitioners in making decisions.

ANSWERS*

4.1 The answer is **D.** Most studies of inpatient medical populations are flawed because of measurement problems, failure to consider the seriousness of the medical illness, and lack of randomization of control and experimental subjects. **(pp. 41–42)**

4.2 The answer is **E.** Cognitive impairment detected during hospitalization predicts nursing home placement within 6 months of discharge. **(p. 40)**

4.3 The answer is **A.** Compared with traditional consultation, liaison psychiatry interventions are more likely to detect significant DSM-III-R psychiatric morbidity. **(p. 42)**

4.4 The answer is **A.** A model of psychiatric training for primary care physicians that is based on the case method is called the consultation model. **(p. 45)**

4.5 The answer is **C.** Forestalling the recurrence of psychiatric or psychological symptoms is accomplished by tertiary prevention. **(p. 43)**

4.6 The answer is **A.** Consultation psychiatry is primarily a secondary prevention effort. **(p. 43)**
The other answers are false; the correct answers are as follows:
The integral model of training relies more on hospital governance than on triage. **(p. 47)**
Prepaid care is associated with decreased detection of and psychosocial counseling for depression in patients. **(p. 48)**

---

*Page numbers within answer sections refer to *The American Psychiatric Press Textbook of Consultation-Liaison Psychiatry.*

4.7   The answer is **D.** Psychiatric clearance is now standard for drug overdose
        patients in the intensive care unit. **(p. 45)**

4.8   The answer is **D.** To improve health care and control costs, the practice
        guidelines formulated by the Agency for Health Care Policy and Research
        focus on assisting patients and practitioners in making decisions. **(p. 48)**

Chapter 5

Basic Science of Neuroimaging and Potential Applications for Consultation-Liaison Psychiatry

Directions: Select the single best response for each of the following questions:

5.1   Currently used neuroimaging modalities are based on detection of
   A. Electroencephalograms (EEGs).
   B. Computerized electroencephalograms.
   C. Computed tomography (CT).
   D. Electromagnetic radiation.
   E. Regional cerebral metabolic rate of glucose.

5.2   The amount of X ray transmitted through the brain depends on
   A. Angle of the X-ray beam.
   B. Density of brain matter.
   C. Frequency of electromagnetic radiation.
   D. Patient's psychiatric history.
   E. Spin lattice relaxation time.

5.3   Currently, most magnetic resonance imaging (MRI) scanners image at the Larmor frequency of the
   A. Carbon atom.
   B. Oxygen atom.
   C. Hydrogen atom.
   D. Helium atom.
   E. Xenon atom.

No corresponding chapter appears in the *Essentials of Consultation-Liaison Psychiatry.*

5.4   The T_1 refers to the time required to regain
       A.   Longitudinal magnetization after a 90-degree radiofrequency pulse.
       B.   The transverse relaxation time of the signal.
       C.   Spin-spin relaxation time.
       D.   All of the above.
       E.   None of the above.

5.5   The nuclei of radiopharmaceuticals emit
       A.   Hydrogen atoms.
       B.   γ Rays.
       C.   Positrons.
       D.   Photons.
       E.   A radiofrequency pulse.

5.6   Indications for using magnetic resonance imaging (MRI) to rule out struc-
       tural brain lesions in patients with primary neurological disorders include
       A.   Connective tissue disorders.
       B.   Central nervous system hemorrhage.
       C.   Toxic encephalopathies.
       D.   All of the above.
       E.   None of the above.

5.7   Atrophy or focal pathology can best be detected in a patient with systemic
       lupus erythematosus using
       A.   Computed tomography (CT).
       B.   Single photon emission computed tomography (SPECT).
       C.   Topographical brain mapping.
       D.   Computerized electroencephalogram.
       E.   Magnetic resonance imaging (MRI).

5.8   Which of the following is false?
       A.   Alzheimer's dementia increases as global and frontal hypometabolism
            develop.
       B.   Electroencephalogram changes regularly accompany diffuse distur-
            bances in brain function.
       C.   Patients with obsessive-compulsive disorder appear to have de-
            creased metabolism in the orbital frontal and/or prefrontal cortex.
       D.   All of the above.
       E.   None of the above.

Directions: For each of the statements below, one or more of the answers is correct. Choose

    A. If 1, 2, and 3 are correct.
    B. If only 1 and 3 are correct.
    C. If only 2 and 4 are correct.
    D. If only 4 is correct.
    E. If all are correct.

5.9   Which modality can detect electromagnetic radiation lower than the human eye can detect?
    1. Magnetic resonance imaging (MRI).
    2. Single photon emission computed tomography (SPECT).
    3. Electroencephalograms (EEGs).
    4. Computed tomography (CT).

5.10   Radiopharmaceuticals used in single photon emission computed tomography (SPECT) include
    1. Xenon.
    2. Hexamethylpropylene amine oxime.
    3. Technetium-99.
    4. Spiperone.

5.11   Positron-emission tomography is one of the most expensive neuroimaging modalities because of
    1. β-Positive decay.
    2. Complex data reduction.
    3. Improved spatial resolution.
    4. On-site cyclotrons.

ANSWERS*

5.1   The answer is **D.** Currently used neuroimaging modalities are based on detection of electromagnetic radiation. **(p. 53)**

5.2   The answer is **B.** The amount of X ray transmitted through the brain depends on the density of brain matter. **(p. 54)**

---

*Page numbers within answer sections refer to *The American Psychiatric Press Textbook of Consultation-Liaison Psychiatry.*

5.3   The answer is **C.** Currently, most magnetic resonance imaging scanners image at the Larmor frequency of the hydrogen atom. **(p. 54)**

5.4   The answer is **A.** The T_1 refers to the time required to regain longitudinal magnetization after a 90-degree radiofrequency pulse. **(pp. 54–55)**

5.5   The answer is **B.** The nuclei of radiopharmaceuticals emit γ rays. **(p. 55)**

5.6   The answer is **D.** Indications for using magnetic resonance imaging to rule out structural brain lesions in patients with primary neurological disorders include connective tissue disorders, hemorrhage, and toxic encephalopathies. **(p. 58)**

5.7   The answer is **E.** Atrophy or focal pathology can best be detected in a patient with systemic lupus erythematosus using magnetic resonance imaging. **(p. 59)**

5.8   The answer is **C.** Patients with obsessive-compulsive disorder appear to have increased metabolism in the orbital frontal and/or prefrontal cortex. **(p. 60)**

5.9   The answer is **B.** Magnetic resonance imaging and electroencephalograms detect electromagnetic radiation lower than the human eye can see. **(p. 53)**

5.10   The answer is **A.** Radiopharmaceuticals used in single photon emission computed tomography include Xenon and technetium-99 (also called hexamethylpropylene amine oxime). **(p. 55)**

5.11   The answer is **D.** Positron-emission tomography is one of the most expensive neuroimaging modalities because of on-site cyclotrons. **(p. 56)**

Chapter 6

Mental Status Examination and Diagnosis

Directions: Select the single best response for each of the following questions:

6.1   Cognitive components of the mental status examination include
   A.   Affect and mood.
   B.   Appearance and behavior.
   C.   Attention.
   D.   All of the above.
   E.   None of the above.

6.2   A 60-year-old man with no psychiatric history who is referred for evaluation of new-onset "schizophrenia" most likely has
   A.   Schizophrenia.
   B.   Major depression.
   C.   Dementia.
   D.   A medical disorder (delirium).
   E.   No serious problems.

6.3   Patients with secondary thought disorders usually have all of the following **EXCEPT**
   A.   Psychiatric history.
   B.   Fluctuating consciousness.
   C.   Disorientation.
   D.   Associated medical illness.
   E.   Older age at onset.

This chapter also corresponds to Chapter 2 in the *Essentials of Consultation-Liaison Psychiatry*.

6.4   Which of the following is false?
       A.   Visual (as opposed to auditory) hallucinations are more typically asso-
            ciated with brain disease.
       B.   Screening mental status examinations are sufficient to detect cognitive
            deficits.
       C.   Olfactory hallucinations are experienced by patients with partial
            seizures.
       D.   All of the above.
       E.   None of the above.

6.5   Attention can best be tested with the
       A.   Bender-Gestalt Test.
       B.   Taylor Equivalent Test.
       C.   Neurobehavioral Cognitive Status Examination.
       D.   Set Test.
       E.   Forward Digit Span.

6.6   Inattention is seen in
       A.   Anxiety.
       B.   Delirium.
       C.   Schizophrenia.
       D.   Mania.
       E.   All of the above.

6.7   In the case of a patient who has poor memory retrieval but is still able to
       learn, damage is most likely to have occurred in the
       A.   Hippocampus.
       B.   Fornix.
       C.   Mamillary bodies.
       D.   Frontal-subcortical structures.
       E.   None of the above.

6.8   Which of the following is true about Folstein's Mini-Mental State Exam?
       A.   It identifies people with focal deficits.
       B.   Patients who have less than an eighth grade education are likely to
            score lower.
       C.   Low scores are not clinically relevant.
       D.   All of the above.
       E.   None of the above.

6.9   Loss or impairment of the ability to use objects correctly is known as
    A. Abulia.
    B. Dysarthria.
    C. Ataxia.
    D. Agnosia.
    E. Apraxia.

Directions: For each of the statements below, one or more of the answers is correct. Choose

    A. If 1, 2, and 3 are correct.
    B. If only 1 and 3 are correct.
    C. If only 2 and 4 are correct.
    D. If only 4 is correct.
    E. If all are correct.

6.10   Terms used to describe a patient's mood include
    1. Euthymic.
    2. Expansive.
    3. Irritable.
    4. Hysterical.

6.11   Parameters used in reporting patients' affect include
    1. Range.
    2. Appearance.
    3. Lability.
    4. Perceptions.

6.12   Medications that can cause depression include
    1. Reserpine.
    2. Trazodone.
    3. α-Methyldopa.
    4. Benzalkonium chloride.

6.13   Language comprehension is intact in
    1. Wernicke's aphasia.
    2. Broca's aphasia.
    3. Global aphasia.
    4. Anomic aphasia.

6.1   The answer is **C.** Attention is a cognitive component of the mental status examination; the other components listed are noncognitive. **(p. 68)**

6.2   The answer is **D.** A 60-year-old man with no psychiatric history who is referred for evaluation of new-onset "schizophrenia" most likely has a medical condition (delirium) or substance-induced disorder. **(p. 68)**

6.3   The answer is **A.** Patients with secondary thought disorders usually have fluctuating consciousness, disorientation, associated medical illness, and older age at onset but do not have a psychiatric history. **(p. 71)**

6.4   The answer is **B.** Screening mental status examinations are not sufficient to detect cognitive deficits. **(p. 72)**

6.5   The answer is **E.** Attention can best be tested with the Forward Digit Span. **(p. 73)**

6.6   The answer is **E.** Inattention is one of the least specific symptoms in psychiatry and is seen in many disorders, including anxiety, delirium, schizophrenia, and mania. **(p. 73)**

6.7   The answer is **D.** In the case of a patient who has poor memory retrieval but is still able to learn, damage is most likely to have occurred in the frontal-subcortical structures. **(p. 76)**

6.8   The answer is **B.** Patients who have less than an eighth grade education are likely to have lower scores on Folstein's Mini-Mental State Exam. **(p. 76)**
       The other answers are false; the correct answers are as follows:
       Folstein's Mini-Mental State Exam cannot identify people with focal deficits very well. **(p. 76)**
       Low scores on Folstein's Mini-Mental State Exam are clinically relevant. **(p. 79)**

6.9   The answer is **E.** Loss or impairment of the ability to use objects correctly is known as apraxia. **(p. 82)**

---

*Page numbers within answer sections refer to *The American Psychiatric Press Textbook of Consultation-Liaison Psychiatry.*

6.10   The answer is **A.** Terms used to describe a patient's mood include euthymic, expansive, and irritable. **(p. 69)**

6.11   The answer is **B.** Parameters used in reporting patients' affect include range and lability. **(p. 69)**

6.12   The answer is **B.** Medications that can cause depression include reserpine and α-methyldopa. **(p. 70)**

6.13   The answer is **C.** Language comprehension is intact in Broca's aphasia and anomic aphasia. **(p. 74)**

Chapter 7

Neuropsychological and Psychological Assessment

Directions: Select the single best response for each of the following questions:

7.1 In Luria's model of brain functioning, Unit 2 of the brain
 A. Is the output unit that produces and controls behavior and motor functioning.
 B. Is the input unit that registers, integrates, and stores sensory information from the visual, auditory, and somatosensory modalities.
 C. Regulates sleep and wakefulness.
 D. Contributes to the overall ability of the brain to function efficiently.
 E. Is located in the frontal lobes.

7.2 Patients who frequently have dysfunction of Unit 1 include all of the following **EXCEPT** those with
 A. Focal cortical brain injury due to trauma.
 B. Huntington's disease.
 C. Delirium.
 D. Parkinson's disease.
 E. Cerebrovascular accidents in the brain stem.

No corresponding chapter appears in the *Essentials of Consultation-Liaison Psychiatry.*

7.3 The battery most frequently used by neuropsychiatrists in clinical practice is the
   A. Mini-Mental State Exam.
   B. Minnesota Multiphasic Personality Inventory.
   C. Personality Assessment Inventory.
   D. Halstead-Reitan Neuropsychological Test Battery.
   E. Luria-Nebraska Neuropsychological Battery.

7.4 A recently developed cognitive screen that can be used at the bedside is the
   A. Luria-Nebraska Neuropsychological Battery.
   B. Seashore Rhythm Test.
   C. BROCAS SCAN.
   D. Halstead-Reitan Neuropsychological Test Battery.
   E. Thematic Apperception Test.

7.5 Which of the following is true?
   A. In the consultation-liaison setting, neuropsychologists are most frequently called on to rule out psychopathology.
   B. Patients with subcortical dementias have memory deficits, language dysfunction or visuospatial impairment, executive deficit, and diminished self-awareness.
   C. Neuropsychological assessment should be performed while the patient is still experiencing posttraumatic amnesia.
   D. All of the above.
   E. None of the above.

7.6 The most widely used and researched objective personality measure is the
   A. Millon Clinical Multiaxial Inventory-III.
   B. Personality Assessment Inventory.
   C. Minnesota Multiphasic Personality Inventory.
   D. Millon Behavioral Health Inventory.
   E. Thematic Apperception Test.

7.7   The classic "conversion V" configuration on the Minnesota Multiphasic Personality Inventory refers to
   A.   Elevation of the depression (D) scale and significantly lower scores on the hypochondriasis (Hs) and hysteria (Hy) scales.
   B.   Elevation of the hypochondriasis (Hs) and hysteria (Hy) scales and significantly lower scores on the depression (D) scale.
   C.   Elevation of the hypochondriasis (Hs) scale and significantly lower scores on the depression (D) and hysteria (Hy) scales.
   D.   Elevation of the hypochondriasis (Hs), hysteria (Hy), and depression (D) scales.
   E.   Significantly lower scores on the hypochondriasis (Hs), hysteria (Hy), and depression (D) scales.

7.8.   Symptom validity testing can be used to assess
   A.   Medicolegal competence.
   B.   Malingering.
   C.   Emotional sequelae of neurological disorders.
   D.   Adjustment of medical illness.
   E.   Reliability.

7.9   Most neuropsychologists
   A.   Identify themselves as clinical psychologists.
   B.   Specialize in a particular disorder.
   C.   Devote 100% of their practice to clinical neuropsychiatry.
   D.   Do all of the above.
   E.   Do none of the above.

Directions: For each of the statements below, one or more of the answers is correct. Choose

   A.   If 1, 2, and 3 are correct.
   B.   If only 1 and 3 are correct.
   C.   If only 2 and 4 are correct.
   D.   If only 4 is correct.
   E.   If all are correct.

7.10   Neuropsychological assessment with a patient-centered approach can be
       conducted using the
       1.   Halstead-Reitan Neuropsychological Test Battery.
       2.   Rorschach Inkblot.
       3.   Luria-Nebraska Neuropsychological Battery.
       4.   Luria's techniques.

7.11   Impairment in auditory learning and memory can result from a deficit in
       1.   Mental control.
       2.   Encoding.
       3.   Language expression.
       4.   Concept formation.

7.12   The Halstead-Reitan Neuropsychological Test Battery includes
       1.   Input measures.
       2.   Output measures.
       3.   Tests of abstraction.
       4.   Tests of verbal abilities.

7.13   In psychological assessment, *validity*
       1.   Refers to consistency within and between administrations and consis-
            tency across raters or scorers.
       2.   Refers to the usefulness of a test.
       3.   Refers to test stability.
       4.   Provides an estimate of the extent to which the test measures the skills
            or qualities it purports to measure.

7.14   The Millon Behavioral Health Inventory is designed to measure
       1.   Compliance with care in medical settings.
       2.   Impact of stress.
       3.   Personality traits.
       4.   Severity of personality disorder.

7.15   Assessment of a patient's general level of distress can best be obtained with
       the
       1.   Beck Depression Inventory (BDI).
       2.   State-Trait Anxiety Inventory.
       3.   Personality Assessment Inventory.
       4.   Profile of Mood States.

ANSWERS*

7.1   The answer is **B.** In Luria's model of brain functioning, Unit 2 of the brain is the input unit that registers, integrates, and stores sensory information from the visual, auditory, and somatosensory modalities. **(p. 88)**

7.2   The answer is **A.** Patients who frequently have dysfunction of Unit 1 include all of the following **EXCEPT** those with focal cortical brain injury due to trauma. **(p. 89)**

7.3   The answer is **D.** The battery most frequently used by neuropsychiatrists in clinical practice is the Halstead-Reitan Neuropsychological Test Battery. **(p. 93)**

7.4   The answer is **C.** A recently developed cognitive screen that can be used at the bedside is the BROCAS SCAN. **(p. 94)**

7.5   The answer is **E.** All of the answers are false; the correct answers are as follows:
        In the consultation-liaison setting, neuropsychologists are most frequently called on to help with differential diagnosis of neuropsychiatric disorders. **(p. 95)**
        Patients with cortical dementias have memory deficits, language dysfunction or visuospatial impairment, executive deficit, and diminished self-awareness. **(p. 95)**
        The value of neuropsychological assessment performed while the patient is still experiencing posttraumatic amnesia is questionable. **(p. 97)**

7.6   The answer is **C.** The most widely used and researched objective personality measure is the Minnesota Multiphasic Personality Inventory. **(p. 100)**

7.7   The answer is **B.** The classic "conversion V" configuration on the Minnesota Multiphasic Personality Inventory refers to elevation of the hypochondriasis (Hs) and hysteria (Hy) scales and significantly lower scores on the depression (D) scale. **(p. 101)**

---

*Page numbers within answer sections refer to *The American Psychiatric Press Textbook of Consultation-Liaison Psychiatry*.

7.8.   The answer is **B.** Symptom validity testing can be used to assess malinger-
        ing. **(p. 107)**

7.9   The answer is **E.** Most neuropsychologists identify themselves as clinical
        neuropsychologists rather than clinical psychologists, are generalists, and
        devote 50% or more of their practice to clinical neuropsychiatry. **(p. 109)**

7.10   The answer is **D.** Neuropsychological assessment with a patient-centered
        approach can be conducted using Luria's techniques. **(p. 91)**

7.11   The answer is **A.** Impairment in auditory learning and memory can result
        from a deficit in mental control, encoding, or language expression. **(p. 92)**

7.12   The answer is **E.** The Halstead-Reitan Neuropsychological Test Battery in-
        cludes input measures, output measures, tests of abstraction, and tests of
        verbal abilities. **(p. 93)**

7.13   The answer is **C.** In psychological assessment, *validity* refers to the useful-
        ness of a test and provides an estimate of the extent to which the test mea-
        sures the skills or qualities it purports to measure. **(p. 99)**

7.14   The answer is **A.** The Millon Behavioral Health Inventory is designed to
        measure compliance with care in medical settings, impact of stress, and
        personality traits. **(p. 102)**

7.15   The answer is **D.** Assessment of a patient's general level of distress can best
        be obtained with the Profile of Mood States. **(pp. 103–104)**

Chapter 8

Behavioral Responses to Illness: Personality and Personality Disorders

Directions: Select the single best response for each of the following questions:

8.1   Apathetic withdrawal is a defense mechanism at the
   A.   Action level.
   B.   Mental inhibitions level.
   C.   Disavowal level.
   D.   Level of defensive dysregulation.
   E.   High adaptive level.

8.2   In treating a self-destructive denier, it is especially important to
   A.   Set clear time limits when scheduling appointments.
   B.   Address feelings of abandonment.
   C.   Treat any underlying depression.
   D.   Help the patient maintain a sense of autonomy.
   E.   Do all of the above.

This chapter also corresponds to Chapter 3 in the *Essentials of Consultation-Liaison Psychiatry.*

8.3   Which of the following is false?

A.   The primary goal of psychiatric consultations with medically ill patients should be psychological growth.

B.   In brief psychotherapy, the consultation-liaison psychiatrist should be careful not to strengthen a patient's defenses.

C.   Medical patients are more likely to develop a transference reaction to the consultation-liaison psychiatrist than to their medical doctor.

D.   All of the above.

E.   None of the above.

8.4   Cardiac patients referred to a consultation-liaison psychiatrist with type A behavior are likely to be characterized by all of the following **EXCEPT**

A.   Noncompetitive.

B.   Hostile.

C.   Impatient.

D.   Muscle tension.

E.   Alert.

8.5   Cluster C DSM-IV Axis II disorders have

A.   Odd or eccentric characteristics.

B.   Anxious or fearful characteristics.

C.   Depressive characteristics.

D.   Dramatic, emotional, or erratic characteristics.

E.   None of the above.

8.6   According to Cloninger's neurotransmitter–personality trait classification system, antisocial personality disorder would reflect

A.   Very high novelty seeking with very low harm avoidance and reward dependence.

B.   Very high harm avoidance with very low novelty seeking and reward dependence.

C.   Very low novelty seeking with very high reward dependence.

D.   Very high novelty seeking, harm avoidance, and reward dependence.

E.   None of the above.

8.7   The DSM-III personality disorder with the highest prevalence in clinical populations of mental health patients is

A.   Obsessive-compulsive.

B.   Self-defeating.

C.   Antisocial.

D.   Avoidant.

E.   Borderline.

8.8 The Axis II diagnosis given the most attention in community samples is
   A. Obsessive-compulsive.
   B. Self-defeating.
   C. Antisocial.
   D. Avoidant.
   E. Borderline.

Directions: For each of the statements below, one or more of the answers is correct. Choose

   A. If 1, 2, and 3 are correct.
   B. If only 1 and 3 are correct.
   C. If only 2 and 4 are correct.
   D. If only 4 is correct.
   E. If all are correct.

8.9 Defense mechanisms classified as major image distorting include
   1. Reaction formation.
   2. Omnipotence.
   3. Anticipation.
   4. Projective identification.

8.10 Patients with alexithymia have
   1. Difficulty experiencing or expressing emotion.
   2. An excellent sense of humor.
   3. A limited ability to communicate distress.
   4. Frequent outbursts of anger.

ANSWERS*

8.1 The answer is **A.** Apathetic withdrawal is a defense mechanism at the action level. **(p. 119)**

8.2 The answer is **C.** In treating a self-destructive denier, it is especially important to treat any underlying depression. **(p. 120)**

---

*Page numbers within answer sections refer to *The American Psychiatric Press Textbook of Consultation-Liaison Psychiatry*.

8.3   The answer is **D.** All of the answers are false; the correct answers are as
        follows:
        The primary goal of psychiatric consultations with medically ill patients
        should be improved adaptation and mastery of the illness situation, rather
        than psychological growth. **(p. 122)**
        In brief psychotherapy, the consultation-liaison psychiatrist usually will
        strengthen a patient's defenses, rather than explore them. **(p. 122)**
        Medical patients are less likely to develop a transference reaction to the
        consultation-liaison psychiatrist than to their medical doctor because they
        have less contact with the psychiatrist. **(p. 123)**

8.4   The answer is **A.** Cardiac patients referred to a consultation-liaison psychi-
        atrist with type A behavior are likely to be characterized by hostility, impa-
        tience, muscle tenseness, alertness, and competitiveness. **(p. 124)**

8.5   The answer is **B.** Cluster C DSM-IV Axis II disorders have anxious or fearful
        characteristics. **(p. 126)**

8.6   The answer is **A.** According to Cloninger's neurotransmitter–personality
        trait classification system, antisocial personality disorder would reflect
        very high novelty seeking with very low harm avoidance and reward de-
        pendence. **(p. 127)**

8.7   The answer is **E.** The DSM-III personality disorder with the highest preva-
        lence in clinical populations of mental health patients is borderline.
        (p. 130)

8.8   The answer is **C.** The Axis II diagnosis given the most attention in commu-
        nity samples is antisocial personality disorder. **(p. 130)**

8.9   The answer is **D.** Defense mechanisms classified as major image distorting
        include projective identification. **(p. 119)**

8.10   The answer is **B.** Patients with alexithymia have difficulty experiencing or
        expressing emotion and a limited ability to communicate distress. **(p. 133)**

Chapter 9

Suicidality

Directions: Select the single best response for each of the following questions:

9.1   Which of the following is false?
   A.   Suicide is the eighth leading cause of death in the United States.
   B.   The suicide rate is three times higher in men than in women.
   C.   The suicide rate for blacks is almost twice that for whites.
   D.   All of the above.
   E.   None of the above.

9.2   Which of the following is true?
   A.   Suicide is the second leading cause of death among adolescents.
   B.   Men are more likely to die from a suicide attempt than are women.
   C.   Suicide rates have tripled in the past three decades.
   D.   All of the above.
   E.   None of the above.

9.3   Psychopathological risk indicators for suicide have the predictive problem of
   A.   Low incidence but high prevalence of suicide.
   B.   High incidence but low prevalence of suicide.
   C.   Low specificity despite high sensitivity.
   D.   High specificity despite low sensitivity.
   E.   Most suicide patients are not identified as psychiatrically ill.

This chapter also corresponds to Chapter 4 in the *Essentials of Consultation-Liaison Psychiatry*.

9.4   Suicide patients are particularly likely to be admitted for inpatient treat-
        ment as a result of an overdose of
        A.   Acetaminophen.
        B.   Antihistamine.
        C.   Alcohol.
        D.   Selective serotonin reuptake inhibitor type antidepressant.
        E.   Narcotic analgesic.

9.5   The percentage of suicide victims who also have physical illness is
        A.   Less than 5%.
        B.   5%–25%.
        C.   26%–75%.
        D.   76%–95%.
        E.   More than 95%.

9.6   Litman noted that the percentage of suicide victims who have some form of
        psychiatric illness is
        A.   10%.
        B.   20%.
        C.   50%.
        D.   75%.
        E.   95%.

9.7   The most common method of suicide in hospitalized patients is
        A.   Overdosing.
        B.   Jumping from a window.
        C.   Slashing wrists.
        D.   Shooting.
        E.   Assisted suicide.

9.8   In cancer patients, the highest relative risk of suicide is
        A.   Just after diagnosis.
        B.   1–2 years after diagnosis.
        C.   2–4 years after diagnosis.
        D.   4–6 years after diagnosis.
        E.   6–10 years after diagnosis.

9.9 Compared with other patients, patients with psychiatric disorders kill themselves at a rate that is
A. Not significantly different.
B. Twice as high.
C. 3–12 times higher.
D. 13–20 times higher.
E. 30 times higher.

9.10 The lifetime risk of suicide is greatest in those with
A. Panic disorder.
B. Panic disorder and depression.
C. Schizophrenia.
D. Psychopathology.
E. Primary mood disorders.

9.11 The psychiatric consultant should admit a suicidal patient to a psychiatric or medical-psychiatric unit
A. In all cases.
B. After interviewing the patient.
C. If it is most cost-effective.
D. If doubts exist about the patient's safety in the outpatient setting.
E. If the patient has a history of suicide attempts.

Directions: For each of the statements below, one or more of the answers is correct. Choose

A. If 1, 2, and 3 are correct.
B. If only 1 and 3 are correct.
C. If only 2 and 4 are correct.
D. If only 4 is correct.
E. If all are correct.

9.12 Definite risk factors for suicide in HIV-infected persons include
1. Adjustment disorder.
2. *Pneumocystis* infection.
3. History of depression.
4. Central nervous system involvement.

9.13   Biological findings in suicide patients include
1.   Platelet serotonin abnormalities.
2.   Increased cerebrospinal fluid serotonin metabolites.
3.   Low cerebrospinal fluid serotonin.
4.   High cerebrospinal fluid 5-hydroxyindoleacetic acid.

9.14   As defined by Litman, presuicidal syndrome is characterized by
1.   Hopelessness.
2.   Long-term predisposition toward impulsive action.
3.   Constricted choices and perceptions.
4.   Physical tension.

ANSWERS[*]

9.1   The answer is **C.** The suicide rate for whites is almost twice that for blacks. **(p. 140)**

9.2   The answer is **D.** All of the statements are true. Suicide is the second leading cause of death among adolescents, men are more likely to die from a suicide attempt than are women, and suicide rates have tripled in the past three decades. **(pp. 140–141)**

9.3   The answer is **C.** Psychopathological risk indicators for suicide have the predictive problem of low specificity despite high sensitivity. **(p. 141)**

9.4   The answer is **A.** Suicide patients are particularly likely to be admitted for inpatient treatment as a result of an overdose of acetaminophen. **(p. 141)**

9.5   The answer is **C.** The percentage of suicide victims who also have physical illness is 26%–75%. **(pp. 141–142)**

9.6   The answer is **E.** Litman noted that the percentage of suicide victims who have some form of psychiatric illness is 95%. **(p. 149)**

9.7   The answer is **B.** The most common method of suicide in hospitalized patients is jumping from a window. **(pp. 142–143)**

---

[*]Page numbers within answer sections refer to *The American Psychiatric Press Textbook of Consultation-Liaison Psychiatry.*

9.8   The answer is **A.** In cancer patients, the highest relative risk of suicide is just after diagnosis. **(pp. 143–144)**

9.9   The answer is **C.** Compared with other patients, patients with psychiatric disorders kill themselves at a rate that is 3–12 times higher. **(p. 145)**

9.10   The answer is **E.** The lifetime risk of suicide is greatest in those with primary mood disorders. **(p. 146)**

9.11   The answer is **D.** A suicidal patient should be admitted to a psychiatric or medical-psychiatric unit if doubts exist about the patient's safety in the outpatient setting. **(p. 155)**

9.12   The answer is **B.** Definite risk factors for suicide in HIV-infected persons include adjustment disorder and history of depression. **(p. 145)**

9.13   The answer is **A.** Biological findings in suicide patients include platelet serotonin abnormalities, increased cerebrospinal fluid serotonin metabolites, and low cerebrospinal fluid serotonin. **(p. 147)**

9.14   The answer is **E.** As defined by Litman, presuicidal syndrome is characterized by hopelessness, long-term predisposition toward impulsive action, constricted choices and perceptions, and physical tension. **(p. 151)**

Chapter 10

Aggression and Agitation

Directions: Select the single best response for each of the following questions:

10.1 In brain-injured patients, aggression is highly prevalent
   A. In the acute recovery stage only.
   B. In the chronic recovery stage only.
   C. In both the acute and the chronic recovery stages.
   D. In the presence of the psychiatrist.
   E. Among outpatients.

10.2 Overt Aggression Scale scores give the most weight to which of the following patient behaviors?
   A. Making loud noises, shouting angrily.
   B. Slamming a door.
   C. Throwing objects onto the floor.
   D. Kicking someone without injuring him or her.
   E. Setting fires.

10.3 Which of the following can cause mania?
   A. Anticholinergics.
   B. Antianxiety agents.
   C. Steroids.
   D. Antipsychotics.
   E. Analgesics.

This chapter also corresponds to Chapter 5 in the *Essentials of Consultation-Liaison Psychiatry*.

10.4   Which of the following is true?
    A.   Aggression secondary to organic aggression syndrome usually does not involve premeditation.
    B.   No medication is currently approved by the Food and Drug Administration (FDA) to treat aggression.
    C.   Neuroleptics are often prescribed for both acute and chronic aggression.
    D.   All of the above.
    E.   None of the above.

10.5   Patients with brain injury have increased sensitivity to the neurotoxic effects of
    A.   Lithium.
    B.   Valproic acid.
    C.   Propranolol.
    D.   Carbamazepine.
    E.   All of the above.

Directions: For each of the statements below, one or more of the answers is correct. Choose

    A.   If 1, 2, and 3 are correct.
    B.   If only 1 and 3 are correct.
    C.   If only 2 and 4 are correct.
    D.   If only 4 is correct.
    E.   If all are correct.

10.6   In DSM-IV, diagnosis of intermittent explosive disorder does not apply if the episodes of aggression
    1.   Are better accounted for by another mental disorder.
    2.   Are the result of a personality disorder or mania.
    3.   Are due to the direct physiological effects of a substance or a general medical condition.
    4.   Are precipitated by little or no provocation.

10.7   Violent behavior is an associated feature of
    1.   Atypical depression.
    2.   Dysthymic disorder.
    3.   Cyclothymic disorder.
    4.   Bipolar disorder.

10.8   Violent behavior is an infrequent feature of
    1.   Paranoid personality disorder.
    2.   Schizoid personality disorder.
    3.   Dissociative fugue.
    4.   Major depressive disorder.

10.9   Acute aggression can be treated with
    1.   β-Blockers.
    2.   Anticonvulsants.
    3.   Antidepressants.
    4.   Benzodiazepines.

ANSWERS*

10.1   The answer is **C.** In brain-injured patients, aggression is highly prevalent in both the acute and the chronic recovery stages. **(p. 163)**

10.2   The answer is **E.** Overt Aggression Scale scores give a weight of 5 to setting fires. **(p. 167)**

10.3   The answer is **C.** Steroids can cause mania. **(p. 169)**

10.4   The answer is **D.** All of the statements are true. Aggression secondary to organic aggression syndrome usually does not involve premeditation. No medication is currently approved by the Food and Drug Administration (FDA) to treat aggression. Neuroleptics are often prescribed for both acute and chronic aggression. **(pp. 170–171)**

10.5   The answer is **A.** Patients with brain injury have increased sensitivity to the neurotoxic effects of lithium. **(p. 174)**

10.6   The answer is **A.** In DSM-IV, diagnosis of intermittent explosive disorder does not apply if the episodes of aggression are better accounted for by another mental disorder, are the result of a personality disorder or mania, or are due to the direct physiological effects of a substance or a general medical condition. **(p. 165)**

---

*Page numbers within answer sections refer to *The American Psychiatric Press Textbook of Consultation-Liaison Psychiatry.*

10.7   The answer is **D.** Violent behavior is an associated feature of bipolar disor-
        der. **(p. 169)**

10.8   The answer is **E.** Violent behavior is an infrequent feature of paranoid per-
        sonality disorder, schizoid personality disorder, dissociative fugue, and
        major depressive disorder. **(p. 169)**

10.9   The answer is **D.** Acute aggression can be treated with benzodiazepines.
        (p. 172)

Chapter 11

Legal and Ethical Issues

Directions: Select the single best response for each of the following questions:

11.1 The three essential ingredients of informed consent are
   A. Emergencies, incompetency, and therapeutic privilege.
   B. Competency, information, and voluntariness.
   C. Right to refuse treatment, self-determination, and information.
   D. Confidentiality, testimonial privilege, and voluntariness.
   E. None of the above.

11.2 Which of the following is Food and Drug Administration (FDA)–approved to treat delirium?
   A. Haloperidol.
   B. Lithium.
   C. Lorazepam.
   D. All of the above.
   E. None of the above.

11.3 Which of the following is false?
   A. Patient values, rather than physician values, are more decisive in end-of-life decisions.
   B. Lack of competency cannot be presumed from treatment of mental illness.
   C. Only competent persons may give informed consent.
   D. All of the above.
   E. None of the above.

This chapter also corresponds to Chapter 6 in the *Essentials of Consultation-Liaison Psychiatry*.

11.4   The landmark case *Youngberg v. Romeo* (1982) pertains to
        A.   Involuntary hospitalization.
        B.   Restraint.
        C.   Informed consent.
        D.   Guardianship.
        E.   Substituted judgment.

11.5   Which of the following is true?
        A.   The consultation-liaison psychiatrist's primary relationship is with the
             patient, not with the physician.
        B.   A consulting psychiatrist should never undertake supervision of a
             nonmedical therapist.
        C.   Psychiatrists must realize that their reponsibilities to patients are lim-
             ited by the contractual arrangements of managed care.
        D.   All of the above.
        E.   None of the above.

11.6   In order for a psychiatrist to be found liable for malpractice, the following
        must be established:
        A.   The psychiatrist was responsible for care.
        B.   A breach in the duty of care occurred.
        C.   The patient experienced actual damages.
        D.   The damages were a direct result of negligence.
        E.   All of the above.

Directions: For each of the statements below, one or more of the answers is
correct. Choose

        A.   If 1, 2, and 3 are correct.
        B.   If only 1 and 3 are correct.
        C.   If only 2 and 4 are correct.
        D.   If only 4 is correct.
        E.   If all are correct.

11.7   Common statutory exceptions to confidentiality between psychiatrist and
        patient include
        1.   Child abuse.
        2.   Court-ordered evaluations.
        3.   Communication with other treatment providers.
        4.   Workers' compensation cases.

11.8   A physician can be held liable for a breach of confidentiality on the basis of
        1. Advance directives.
        2. Malpractice.
        3. Right to refuse treatment.
        4. Invasion of privacy.

11.9   Fluoxetine is Food and Drug Administration (FDA)–approved for the treatment of
        1. Premature ejaculation.
        2. Premenstrual syndrome.
        3. Smoking cessation.
        4. Obsessive-compulsive disorder.

11.10   The President's Commission for the Study of Ethical Problems in Medicine
        and Biomedical and Behavioral Research recommends that relatives of in-
        competent patients be selected as proxy decision makers because
        1. The family is most knowledgeable about the patient's goals, prefer-
            ences, and values.
        2. The family deserves recognition as an important social unit.
        3. The family is generally most concerned about the good of the patient.
        4. Decision making by the family is expedient.

ANSWERS[*]

11.1   The answer is **B.** The three essential ingredients of informed consent are
        competency, information, and voluntariness. **(p. 182)**

11.2   The answer is **E.** No agents have been approved by the Food and Drug Ad-
        ministration (FDA) to treat delirium. **(p. 184)**

11.3   The answer is **A.** Despite the growing use of advance directives, increasing
        evidence suggests that physician values, rather than patient values, are
        more decisive in end-of-life decisions. **(p. 188)**

11.4   The answer is **B.** The landmark case *Youngberg v. Romeo* (1982) pertains to
        restraint. **(p. 193)**

---

[*]Page numbers within answer sections refer to *The American Psychiatric Press Textbook
of Consultation-Liaison Psychiatry.*

11.5   The answer is **E.** None of the answers is true; the correct answers are as follows:

The consultation-liaison psychiatrist's primary relationship is with the physician, not with the patient. **(p. 194)**

If he or she is prepared to assume medical responsibility for the patient, a consulting psychiatrist can undertake supervision of a nonmedical therapist. **(p. 195)**

Psychiatrists must realize that their reponsibilities to patients are not limited by the contractual arrangements of managed care. **(p. 196)**

11.6   The answer is **E.** In order for a psychiatrist to be found liable for malpractice, it must be established that the psychiatrist was responsible for care, a breach in the duty of care occurred, the patient experienced actual damages, and the damages were a direct result of negligence. **(p. 197)**

11.7   The answer is **A.** Common statutory exceptions to confidentiality between psychiatrist and patient include child abuse, court-ordered evaluations, and communication with other treatment providers. **(p. 181)**

11.8   The answer is **C.** A physician can be held liable for a breach of confidentiality on the basis of malpractice and invasion of privacy. **(pp. 181–182)**

11.9   The answer is **D.** Fluoxetine is Food and Drug Administration (FDA)–approved for the treatment of obsessive-compulsive disorder. **(p. 184)**

11.10   The answer is **A.** The President's Commission for the Study of Ethical Problems in Medicine and Biomedical and Behavioral Research recommends that relatives of incompetent patients be selected as proxy decision makers because the family is most knowledgeable about the patient's goals, preferences, and values; the family deserves recognition as an important social unit; and the family is generally most concerned about the good of the patient. **(p. 190)**

Chapter 12

Consultation-Liaison Psychiatry Research

Directions: Select the single best response for each of the following questions:

12.1   The effectiveness of a new drug can be evaluated with minimal potential bias using
   A.   Basic science research.
   B.   Case studies.
   C.   Clinical intervention studies.
   D.   Cross-sectional population descriptive studies.
   E.   Cohort studies.

12.2   Prefrontal cortex lesions can cause difficulties with all of the following **EXCEPT**
   A.   Language comprehension.
   B.   Stimulus-bound behavior.
   C.   Abstraction.
   D.   Temporal ordering.
   E.   Fluency.

12.3   Neuroscience research has hypothesized that an unwanted second-messenger signal could explain the signs and symptoms of
   A.   Dementia.
   B.   Mania.
   C.   Parkinson's disease.
   D.   Pick's disease.
   E.   Somatoform disorders.

No corresponding chapter appears in the *Essentials of Consultation-Liaison Psychiatry*.

12.4   A mistake commonly made in cross-sectional epidemiology studies is
        A.   Underestimating the necessary sample size.
        B.   Deliberate oversampling.
        C.   Using a representative study sample.
        D.   Lack of stratified sampling.
        E.   Using only a single measurement.

12.5   Cohort studies are valuable for
        A.   Determining syndrome prevalence rates.
        B.   Comparing prevalence rates.
        C.   Making retrospective comparisons.
        D.   Evaluating the effectiveness of an intervention.
        E.   Identifying risk factors.

12.6   In order to conclusively establish a causal relationship between a consulta-
        tion-liaison psychiatry intervention and cost savings resulting from im-
        proved health care utilization, the research methodology must include
        A.   Confounding bias.
        B.   Outcome measures that apply to the system of care rather than to the
             individual patient.
        C.   Almost identical control and intervention groups.
        D.   Descriptive analyses.
        E.   A large study sample.

12.7   The Hawthorne effect refers to
        A.   Recall bias.
        B.   Expectation bias.
        C.   Unacceptability bias.
        D.   Nonresponse bias.
        E.   Attention bias.

Directions: For each of the statements below, one or more of the answers is correct. Choose

    A.   If 1, 2, and 3 are correct.
    B.   If only 1 and 3 are correct.
    C.   If only 2 and 4 are correct.
    D.   If only 4 is correct.
    E.   If all are correct.

12.8   Since 1980, empirically based research in the field of consultation-liaison psychiatry
    1.   Has become less costly.
    2.   Has replaced case studies.
    3.   Has provided definitive practice guidelines for clinicians.
    4.   Has more than doubled, in terms of the number of publications.

12.9   Clinically available functional neuroimaging includes
    1.   Computed tomography (CT).
    2.   Magnetic resonance imaging (MRI).
    3.   Topographical brain mapping.
    4.   Single photon emission computed tomography (SPECT).

12.10   The value of a single case study can be enhanced by
    1.   Obtaining repeated measurements until reasonable stability is achieved.
    2.   Recording and accounting for potentially confounding events that could affect findings.
    3.   Using the scientific method of hypothesis testing whenever possible.
    4.   Generalizing the findings.

12.11   The purpose of a secondary intervention is to
    1.   Prevent a disorder.
    2.   Reduce the duration of an illness.
    3.   Reduce morbidity associated with an illness.
    4.   Reduce the prevalence of an illness.

ANSWERS*

12.1   The answer is **C**. The effectiveness of a new drug can be evaluated with minimal potential bias using clinical intervention studies. **(p. 210)**

12.2   The answer is **A**. Prefrontal cortex lesions can cause difficulties with stimulus-bound behavior, abstraction, temporal ordering, and fluency. **(p. 211)**

12.3   The answer is **B**. Neuroscience research has hypothesized that an unwanted second-messenger signal could explain the signs and symptoms of mania. **(p. 211)**

12.4   The answer is **A**. A mistake commonly made in cross-sectional epidemiology studies is underestimating the necessary sample size. **(p. 215)**

12.5   The answer is **E**. Cohort studies are valuable for identifying risk factors. **(p. 217)**

12.6   The answer is **C**. In order to conclusively establish a causal relationship between a consultation-liaison psychiatry intervention and cost savings resulting from improved health care utilization, the research methodology must include almost identical control and intervention groups. **(p. 220)**

12.7   The answer is **E**. The Hawthorne effect refers to attention bias. **(p. 221)**

12.8   The answer is **D**. Since 1980, empirically based research in the field of consultation-liaison psychiatry has more than doubled, in terms of the number of publications. **(p. 208)**

12.9   The answer is **D**. Clinically available functional neuroimaging includes single photon emission computed tomography. **(p. 212)**

12.10   The answer is **A**. The value of a single case study can be enhanced by obtaining repeated measurements until reasonable stability is achieved, recording and accounting for potentially confounding events that could affect findings, and using the scientific method of hypothesis testing whenever possible. **(p. 214)**

12.11   The answer is **C**. The purpose of a secondary intervention is to reduce the duration or prevalence of an illness. **(p. 218)**

---

*Page numbers within answer sections refer to *The American Psychiatric Press Textbook of Consultation-Liaison Psychiatry*.

Chapter 13

International Perspectives on Consultation-Liaison Psychiatry

Directions: Select the single best response for each of the following questions:

13.1 According to Wallen, average consultation rates in nonacademic general hospitals in the United States are
   A. 0.2%.
   B. 0.8%.
   C. 1.0%.
   D. 2.0%.
   E. 8.0%.

13.2 Psychosomatics has been most highly institutionalized in
   A. The Nordic countries.
   B. The United Kingdom.
   C. Australia.
   D. Germany.
   E. The United States.

13.3 Which of the following is true?
   A. Consultation-liaison services in Europe are usually satellites of psychiatric departments.
   B. Institutionalized psychosomatics occurred first in academic hospitals.
   C. Fully integrated services with early screening are rare.
   D. All of the above.
   E. None of the above.

No corresponding chapter appears in the *Essentials of Consultation-Liaison Psychiatry.*

13.4   Which of the following was formed in 1992 to provide a formal structure
        for international collaboration?
        A.   European Consultation-Liaison Workshop for General Hospital Psy-
              chiatry and Psychosomatics (ECLW).
        B.   European Association for Consultation-Liaison Psychiatry and
              Psychosomatics (EACLPP).
        C.   Netherlands Consortium for Consultation-Liaison Psychiatry (NCCP).
        D.   Japanese Society of General Hospital Psychiatry (JSGHP).
        E.   MICRO-CARES.

13.5   Multicentered, international research has shown that, compared with pa-
        tients who were not referred, patients referred by consultation-liaison ser-
        vices had on average
        A.   Hospital stays of equal length.
        B.   Two to three times shorter hospital stays.
        C.   Two to three times longer hospital stays.
        D.   Fewer hospitalizations.
        E.   Twice as many hospitalizations.

13.6   Which of the following is false?
        A.   Only 15% of general hospitals in Germany have in-hospital mental
              health services.
        B.   There are approximately 125 full-time consultation-liaison psychia-
              trists in the United Kingdom.
        C.   There are no psychosomatic wards in the southern European and
              Mediterranean countries.
        D.   All of the above.
        E.   None of the above.

Directions: For each of the statements below, one or more of the answers is correct. Choose

    A.   If 1, 2, and 3 are correct.
    B.   If only 1 and 3 are correct.
    C.   If only 2 and 4 are correct.
    D.   If only 4 is correct.
    E.   If all are correct.

13.7   Tax-financed health insurance is found in
    1.   The United Kingdom.
    2.   Portugal.
    3.   Scandinavia.
    4.   Spain.

13.8   The patient registration form measures
    1.   Referral characteristics.
    2.   Up to 10 psychiatric diagnoses.
    3.   Consultation-liaison input time.
    4.   Personnel characteristics.

ANSWERS*

13.1   The answer is **A.** According to Wallen, average consultation rates in nonacademic general hospitals in the United States are 0.2%. **(p. 230)**

13.2   The answer is **D.** Psychosomatics has been most highly institutionalized in Germany. **(p. 231)**

13.3   The answer is **D.** All of the statements are true. Consultation-liaison services in Europe are usually satellites of psychiatric departments. Institutionalized psychosomatics occurred first in academic hospitals. Fully integrated services with early screening are rare. **(pp. 231–232)**

13.4   The answer is **B.** The European Association for Consultation-Liaison Psychiatry and Psychosomatics (EACLPP) was formed in 1992 to provide a formal structure for international collaboration. **(p. 247)**

---

*Page numbers within answer sections refer to *The American Psychiatric Press Textbook of Consultation-Liaison Psychiatry*.

13.5   The answer is **C.** Multicentered, international research has shown that, compared with patients who were not referred, patients referred by consultation-liaison services had on average two to three times longer hospital stays. **(p. 249)**

13.6   The answer is **B.** There is only a small number (probably less than 10) of full-time consultation-liaison psychiatrists in the United Kingdom. **(p. 238)**

13.7   The answer is **E.** Tax-financed health insurance is found in the United Kingdom, Portugal, Scandinavia, and Spain. **(p. 233)**

13.8   The answer is **B.** The patient registration form measures referral characteristics and consultation-liaison input time. **(p. 248)**

Section II

Psychiatric Disorders in General Hospital Patients

Chapter 14

Delirium (Confusional States)

QUESTIONS

Directions: Select the single best response for each of the following questions:

14.1 The prevalence of delirium in a general hospital is estimated to be
   A. 5%–10%.
   B. 11%–16%.
   C. 17%–22%.
   D. 23%–28%.
   E. 29%–34%.

14.2 A patient who is delirious because of severe hypoglycemia would be given a diagnosis of
   A. Substance-induced delirium.
   B. Delirium due to multiple etiologies.
   C. Delirium due to a general medical condition.
   D. Delirium not otherwise specified.
   E. Delirium not elsewhere classified.

14.3 All of the following increase a patient's risk of delirium **EXCEPT**
   A. High serum albumin.
   B. Brain damage related to HIV infection.
   C. Age over 60.
   D. Severe burn injury.
   E. Drug withdrawal.

This chapter also corresponds to Chapter 7 in the *Essentials of Consultation-Liaison Psychiatry.*

14.4   Which of the following is false?
        A.   Dysnomia is not specific to delirium.
        B.   Delirium has a slow onset.
        C.   Dysgraphia is common in delirium.
        D.   All of the above.
        E.   None of the above.

14.5   The most useful diagnostic laboratory measure for delirium is
        A.   Positron-emission tomography.
        B.   Single photon emission computed tomography (SPECT).
        C.   Computed tomography (CT).
        D.   Skull series.
        E.   Electroencephalogram (EEG).

14.6   The drug of first choice for delirium is
        A.   Droperidol.
        B.   Haloperidol.
        C.   Buspirone.
        D.   Carbamazepine.
        E.   Lithium.

14.7   The majority of patients who experience delirium
        A.   Die within 6 months.
        B.   Progress to stupor.
        C.   Commit suicide.
        D.   Have seizures.
        E.   Have a full recovery.

Directions: For each of the statements below, one or more of the answers is correct. Choose

        A.   If 1, 2, and 3 are correct.
        B.   If only 1 and 3 are correct.
        C.   If only 2 and 4 are correct.
        D.   If only 4 is correct.
        E.   If all are correct.

14.8   Compared with nondelirious patients, patients with delirium have
        1.   An increased use of hospital resources.
        2.   An increased frequency of postsurgical complications.
        3.   Longer hospitalizations.
        4.   A lower mortality rate.

14.9   Prodromal features of delirium include
1. Hyperventilation.
2. Sleep disruption.
3. Vitamin B deficiency.
4. Anxiety.

14.10   Common emotional responses seen in patients with delirium include
1. Anger.
2. Depression.
3. Fear.
4. Euphoria.

14.11   Laboratory work that should be ordered for almost every patient with delirium includes
1. Blood chemistries.
2. Heavy metal screen.
3. Urine drug screen.
4. Electroencephalogram (EEG).

14.12   Psychological support for patients with delirium can be provided by
1. Reassuring the patient that the condition is transient.
2. The presence of a calm family member.
3. Close supervision by nursing staff.
4. Placing the patient in a room with another patient with delirium.

ANSWERS*

14.1   The answer is **B.** The prevalence of delirium in a general hospital is estimated to be 11%–16%. **(p. 261)**

14.2   The answer is **C.** A patient who is delirious because of severe hypoglycemia would be given a diagnosis of delirium due to a general medical condition. **(p. 260)**

14.3   The answer is **A.** Patients who have an increased risk of delirium include those with a low serum albumin, brain damage related to HIV infection, age over 60, severe burn injury, and drug withdrawal. **(pp. 261–262)**

---

*Page numbers within answer sections refer to *The American Psychiatric Press Textbook of Consultation-Liaison Psychiatry.*

14.4   The answer is **B.** Delirium has an abrupt onset. **(p. 262)**

14.5   The answer is **E.** The most useful diagnostic laboratory measure for delirium is the electroencephalogram. **(p. 266)**

14.6   The answer is **B.** The drug of first choice for delirium is haloperidol. **(p. 269)**

14.7   The answer is **E.** The majority of patients who experience delirium have a full recovery. **(p. 270)**

14.8   The answer is **A.** Patients with delirium have an increased use of hospital resources, increased frequency of postsurgical complications, and longer hospitalizations. Delirious patients also have a high mortality rate. **(p. 259, p. 271)**

14.9   The answer is **C.** Prodromal features of delirium include sleep disruption and anxiety. **(p. 262)**

14.10   The answer is **A.** Common emotional responses seen in patients with delirium include anger, depression, and fear. **(p. 265)**

14.11   The answer is **B.** Laboratory work that should be ordered for almost every patient with delirium includes blood chemistries and urine drug screen. **(pp. 266–267)**

14.12   The answer is **A.** Psychological support for delirium patients can be provided by reassuring the patient that the condition is transient, the presence of a calm family member, and close supervision by nursing staff. **(p. 270)**

Chapter 15

Dementia

Directions: Select the single best response for each of the following questions:

15.1 Which of the following is true?
   A. Dementia is irreversible.
   B. Dementia can be the result of normal aging.
   C. Dementia of the Alzheimer's type is an example of subcortical dementia.
   D. All of the above.
   E. None of the above.

15.2 Vascular dementia is often cited as an example of a
   A. Cortical dementia.
   B. Subcortical dementia.
   C. Mixed dementia.
   D. Pseudodementia.
   E. Toxic-metabolic dementia.

15.3 The number of Americans with severe dementia is estimated to be
   A. 1 million.
   B. 2 million.
   C. 4 million.
   D. 10 million.
   E. 20 million.

This chapter also corresponds to Chapter 8 in the *Essentials of Consultation-Liaison Psychiatry*.

15.4   The most commonly occurring dementia is
        A.   Dementia of the Alzheimer's type.
        B.   Vascular dementia.
        C.   Lewy body dementia.
        D.   Alcoholic dementia.
        E.   HIV-related dementia.

15.5   According to DSM-IV, diagnosis of dementia of the Alzheimer's type is
        made using all of the following **EXCEPT**
        A.   Apraxia.
        B.   Frontal release signs.
        C.   Agnosia.
        D.   Aphasia.
        E.   Disturbance in executive functioning.

15.6   Loss of volitional down gaze, postural instability and falling, gait abnor-
        malities, and depression are common presenting symptoms of
        A.   Limbic encephalopathy.
        B.   Wilson's disease.
        C.   Progressive supranuclear palsy.
        D.   Pick's disease.
        E.   None of the above.

15.7   Abrupt onset, stepwise progression, fluctuating course, depression, his-
        tory of stroke, and evidence of atherosclerosis characterize
        A.   Limbic encephalopathy.
        B.   Wilson's disease.
        C.   Progressive supranuclear palsy.
        D.   Pick's disease.
        E.   None of the above.

15.8   The most common dementia associated with infectious disease is
        A.   HIV-1-associated minor cognitive/motor disorder.
        B.   HIV-1-associated dementia complex.
        C.   Progressive multifocal leukoencephalopathy.
        D.   Chronic meningitis.
        E.   Creutzfeldt-Jakob disease.

15.9 The largest group of patients with toxic-metabolic dementia are those with
  A. Porphyria.
  B. Anoxia.
  C. Wernicke-Korsakoff syndrome.
  D. Alcoholism.
  E. None of the above.

15.10 Prions cause
  A. HIV-associated dementia.
  B. Pernicious anemia.
  C. Creutzfeldt-Jakob disease.
  D. Endocrine-related dementia.
  E. Wernicke-Korsakoff syndrome.

15.11 The preferred instrument for staging of dementia is
  A. Executive Interview (EXIT).
  B. Mini-Mental State Exam (MMSE).
  C. Neuropsychiatric Inventory (NPI).
  D. Clinical Dementia Rating (CDR) scale.
  E. Millon Clinical Multiaxial Inventory-II (MCMI-II).

Directions: For each of the statements below, one or more of the answers is correct. Choose

  A. If 1, 2, and 3 are correct.
  B. If only 1 and 3 are correct.
  C. If only 2 and 4 are correct.
  D. If only 4 is correct.
  E. If all are correct.

15.12 Subcortical dementias include
  1. Huntington's disease.
  2. Pick's disease.
  3. Parkinson's disease.
  4. Alzheimer's dementia.

15.13 Risk factors for dementia include
  1. Family history of dementia.
  2. Head trauma.
  3. The apolipoprotein-e-4 allele.
  4. Low level of education.

15.14   Neuroimaging is valuable in diagnosing
1.   Dementia of the Alzheimer's type.
2.   HIV-1 dementia.
3.   Vascular dementia.
4.   Frontal lobe dementia.

15.15   Medical management of dementias includes
1.   Haloperidol.
2.   Loxapine.
3.   Aspirin.
4.   Lithium.

ANSWERS*

15.1   The answer is **E.** All of the answers are false; the correct answers are as follows:
Although some dementias are chronic, dementia does not automatically imply irreversibility. **(p. 277)**
Dementia reflects the effect of pathological processes on the brain and is not the result of normal aging. **(p. 277)**
Dementia of the Alzheimer's type is an example of cortical dementia. **(p. 278)**

15.2   The answer is **C.** Vascular dementia is often cited as an example of a mixed dementia. **(p. 279)**

15.3   The answer is **C.** The number of Americans with severe dementia is estimated to be 4 million. **(p. 280)**

15.4   The answer is **A.** The most commonly occurring dementia is dementia of the Alzheimer's type. **(p. 280)**

15.5   The answer is **B.** According to DSM-IV, diagnosis of dementia of the Alzheimer's type is made using one or more of the following: apraxia, agnosia, aphasia, and disturbance in executive functioning. **(p. 282)**

---

*Page numbers within answer sections refer to *The American Psychiatric Press Textbook of Consultation-Liaison Psychiatry.*

15.6   The answer is **C.** Loss of volitional down gaze, postural instability and falling, gait abnormalities, and depression are common presenting symptoms of progressive supranuclear palsy. **(p. 284)**

15.7   The answer is **E.** Abrupt onset, stepwise progression, fluctuating course, depression, history of stroke, and evidence of atherosclerosis characterize vascular dementia. **(p. 284)**

15.8   The answer is **B.** The most common dementia associated with infectious disease is HIV-1-associated dementia complex. **(p. 286)**

15.9   The answer is **D.** The largest group of patients with toxic-metabolic dementia are those with alcoholism. **(p. 287)**

15.10   The answer is **C.** Prions cause Creutzfeldt-Jakob disease. **(p. 292)**

15.11   The answer is **D.** The preferred instrument for staging of dementia is the Clinical Dementia Rating scale (CDR). **(p. 299)**

15.12   The answer is **B.** Subcortical dementias include Huntington's disease and Parkinson's disease. **(p. 279)**

15.13   The answer is **E.** Risk factors for dementia include a family history of dementia, head trauma, inheritance of the apolipoprotein-e-4 allele, and a low level of education. **(p. 281)**

15.14   The answer is **E.** Neuroimaging is valuable in diagnosing dementia of the Alzheimer's type, HIV-1 dementia, vascular dementia, and frontal lobe dementia. **(pp. 297–298)**

15.15   The answer is **A.** Medical management of dementias includes haloperidol, loxapine, and aspirin. **(pp. 300–302)**

Chapter 16

Depression

Directions: Select the single best response for each of the following questions:

16.1   According to Rifkin, the most common cause for underdiagnosis and undertreatment of depression in medically ill patients is
   A.   Primary care physicians who have inadequate training in psychiatry.
   B.   The belief that depression is not pathological in these patients.
   C.   The low prevalence of depression in these patients.
   D.   The patient's emphasis on somatic rather than cognitive or mood complaints.
   E.   Fear of antidepressant side effects.

16.2   The percentage of psychiatric patients with a major medical problem that has not been detected by the referring physician is
   A.   6%.
   B.   16%.
   C.   26%.
   D.   36%.
   E.   46%.

This chapter also corresponds to Chapter 9 in the *Essentials of Consultation-Liaison Psychiatry*.

16.3   Among the following conditions, the development of major depression is
        most likely following a diagnosis of
        A. Cancer.
        B. Stroke.
        C. Hemodialysis.
        D. Epilepsy.
        E. Chronic pain.

16.4   Which of the following is true?
        A. Most patients with primary depression have a positive history for
            mood disorders.
        B. Up to 60% of depressed patients have decreased rapid eye movement
            latency.
        C. The suicide rate among depressed dialysis patients is as much as 400
            times that of the general population.
        D. All of the above.
        E. None of the above.

16.5   The finding that clinical depression typically causes hypercortisolism has
        led to the development of which of the following measures?
        A. Thyroid-stimulating hormone levels.
        B. Thyrotropin-releasing hormone suppression test.
        C. Dexamethasone suppression test.
        D. Platelet imipramine binding.
        E. Rapid eye movement latency.

16.6   Following a stroke, the high-risk period for depression extends for
        A. 2 months.
        B. 6 months.
        C. 12 months.
        D. 18 months.
        E. 24 months.

16.7   Which of the following is false?
        A. AIDS patients are especially sensitive to anticholinergic side effects.
        B. Multiple sclerosis patients with predominantly spinal disease have in-
            creased rates of depression compared with multiple sclerosis patients
            who have predominantly cerebral disease.
        C. A previous episode of depression is the most reliable predictor of re-
            serpine-induced depression.
        D. All of the above.
        E. None of the above.

16.8 According to Schuckit's research, most alcohol-induced depressions resolve within
    A. 1 week following abstinence.
    B. 2 weeks following abstinence.
    C. 1 month following abstinence.
    D. 2 months following abstinence.
    E. 6 months following abstinence.

16.9 Following diagnosis of depression in a medically ill patient, the initial step in treatment of depression is
    A. Identification of causative toxic or medical factors.
    B. Identification of biological markers.
    C. Hospitalization.
    D. Initiation of psychotherapy.
    E. Initiation of pharmacological treatment.

16.10 In cases of treatment-resistant depression, the clinician's first action should be to
    A. Terminate therapy.
    B. Begin electroconvulsive therapy (ECT).
    C. Augment the current medication with a second drug.
    D. Increase the dose of the current antidepressant medication.
    E. Change medications.

Directions: For each of the statements below, one or more of the answers is correct. Choose

    A. If 1, 2, and 3 are correct.
    B. If only 1 and 3 are correct.
    C. If only 2 and 4 are correct.
    D. If only 4 is correct.
    E. If all are correct.

16.11 Compared with primary major depression, depression secondary to medical illness is characterized by
    1. Older age at onset.
    2. An increased likelihood to commit suicide.
    3. A decreased likelihood of a family history of alcoholism.
    4. A decreased likelihood to respond to electroconvulsive therapy (ECT).

16.12 Which of the following medications can cause depression?
1. Methyldopa.
2. Cimetidine.
3. Procarbazine.
4. Docusate.

16.13 Psychotropic medications that have potent anticholinergic properties include
1. Haloperidol.
2. Thioridazine.
3. Trazodone.
4. Amitriptyline.

16.14 Tricyclic antidepressants should be avoided in patients with
1. Insomnia.
2. Second-degree heart block.
3. Hypertension.
4. A corrected Q-T greater than 440 msec.

16.15 Electroconvulsive therapy (ECT) is considered the treatment of choice for patients who have
1. Delusional depression.
2. Failed treatment with antidepressants.
3. Severe malnutrition and depression.
4. Depression and are pregnant.

16.16 Typical goals for brief psychotherapy with depressed patients include
1. Reduce isolation.
2. Improve self-esteem.
3. Facilitate the expression of fears.
4. Understand unconscious causes of depression.

ANSWERS*

16.1 The answer is **B.** According to Rifkin, the most common cause for underdiagnosis and undertreatment of depression in medically ill patients is the belief that depression is not pathological in these patients. **(p. 311)**

---

*Page numbers within answer sections refer to *The American Psychiatric Press Textbook of Consultation-Liaison Psychiatry.*

16.2 The answer is **E.** The percentage of psychiatric patients with a major medical problem that has not been detected by the referring physician is 46%. **(p. 312)**

16.3 The answer is **D.** The development of major depression is most likely following a diagnosis of epilepsy. **(p. 315)**

16.4 The answer is **D.** All of the statements are true. Most patients with primary depression have a positive history for mood disorders. Up to 60% of depressed patients have decreased rapid eye movement latency. The suicide rate among depressed dialysis patients is as much as 400 times that of the general population. **(pp. 319–321)**

16.5 The answer is **C.** The finding that clinical depression typically causes hypercortisolism has led to the development of the dexamethasone suppression test. **(p. 321)**

16.6 The answer is **E.** Following a stroke, the high-risk period for depression extends for 24 months. **(p. 323)**

16.7 The answer is **B.** Multiple sclerosis patients with predominantly cerebral disease have increased rates of depression compared with multiple sclerosis patients who have predominantly spinal disease. **(p. 327)**

16.8 The answer is **B.** According to Schuckit's research, most alcohol-induced depressions resolve within 2 weeks following abstinence. **(p. 332)**

16.9 The answer is **A.** Following diagnosis of depression in a medically ill patient, the initial step in treatment is identification of causative toxic or medical factors. **(pp. 332–333)**

16.10 The answer is **D.** In cases of treatment-resistant depression, the clinician's first action should be to increase the dose of the current antidepressant medication. **(p. 336)**

16.11 The answer is **B.** Compared with primary major depression, depression secondary to medical illness is characterized by older age at onset and less likelihood of having a family history of alcoholism. **(p. 315)**

16.12 The answer is **A.** Depression can be caused by methyldopa, cimetidine, and procarbazine. **(p. 318)**

16.13 The answer is **C.** Psychotropic medications that have potent anti-cholinergic properties include thioridazine and amitriptyline. **(p. 333)**

16.14 The answer is **C.** Tricyclic antidepressants should be avoided in patients with second-degree heart block and a corrected Q-T greater than 440 msec. **(p. 334)**

16.15 The answer is **E.** Electroconvulsive therapy is considered the treatment of choice for patients who have delusional depression, have failed treatment with antidepressants, have severe malnutrition and depression, and have depression and are pregnant. **(p. 337)**

16.16 The answer is **A.** Typical goals for brief psychotherapy with depressed patients include reducing isolation, improving self-esteem, and facilitating the expression of fears. **(p. 338)**

Chapter 17

Mania

QUESTIONS

Directions: Select the single best response for each of the following questions:

17.1 A mood syndrome characterized by one or more manic episodes usually accompanied by one or more major depressive episodes is
A. Secondary mania.
B. Primary mania.
C. Bipolar disorder.
D. Cyclothymia.
E. Hypomania.

17.2 In primary bipolar disorder, manic episodes rarely occur after age
A. 30.
B. 40.
C. 50.
D. 60.
E. 70.

17.3 A manic episode is most likely to begin with
A. Paranoid delusions.
B. Hallucinations.
C. Trauma.
D. Mild hypermania.
E. Suicide attempt.

This chapter also corresponds to Chapter 10 in the *Essentials of Consultation-Liaison Psychiatry.*

17.4   A deficit of catecholamines is associated with
        A. Depression.
        B. Mania.
        C. Euphoria.
        D. Anxiety.
        E. Bipolar disorder.

17.5   Which of the following medications is most likely to cause secondary
        mania?
        A. Captopril.
        B. Bromide.
        C. Zidovudine.
        D. Hallucinogens.
        E. Decongestants containing phenylephrine.

17.6   The most widely used antimanic agent is
        A. Valproic acid.
        B. Clonazepam.
        C. Carbamazepine.
        D. Lithium.
        E. Haloperidol.

17.7   Which of the following is true?
        A. The side effects of lithium are usually mild and transient.
        B. Anticonvulsants cannot be used in combination with lithium.
        C. Carbamazepine inhibits liver enzymes.
        D. All of the above.
        E. None of the above.

17.8   The ideal setting for treating patients with secondary mania is
        A. Inpatient psychiatric unit.
        B. Outpatient.
        C. Medical-psychiatric unit.
        D. Group psychotherapy.
        E. None of the above.

Directions: For each of the statements below, one or more of the answers is
correct. Choose

        A. If 1, 2, and 3 are correct.
        B. If only 1 and 3 are correct.

C. If only 2 and 4 are correct.
D. If only 4 is correct.
E. If all are correct.

17.9 DSM-IV criteria for a diagnosis of a manic episode include the following symptoms:
1. Low self-esteem.
2. Less talkative than usual.
3. Decreased goal-directed activity.
4. Decreased need for sleep.

17.10 A higher total lifetime number of manic episodes is associated with
1. Family history of mood disorder.
2. Shorter duration of episodes.
3. Earlier age at onset.
4. Lower socioeconomic status.

17.11 In right-handed persons, risk of depression is associated with
1. Left frontotemporal lesions.
2. Right frontotemporal lesions.
3. Right parietooccipital lesions.
4. Left parietooccipital lesions.

17.12 Electroconvulsive therapy (ECT) is indicated for manic patients who are
1. Unresponsive to antimanic agents.
2. At high risk for suicide.
3. Severely manic.
4. Being treated with lithium.

ANSWERS*

17.1 The answer is **C.** A mood syndrome characterized by one or more manic episodes usually accompanied by one or more major depressive episodes is bipolar disorder. **(p. 347)**

17.2 The answer is **C.** In primary bipolar disorder, manic episodes rarely occur after age 50. **(p. 349)**

---

*Page numbers within answer sections refer to *The American Psychiatric Press Textbook of Consultation-Liaison Psychiatry*.

17.3   The answer is **D.** A manic episode is most likely to begin with mild hypermania. **(p. 350)**

17.4   The answer is **A.** A deficit of catecholamines is associated with depression. **(p. 352)**

17.5   The answer is **E.** Decongestants containing phenylephrine are more likely to cause secondary mania than the other medications listed. **(pp. 354–355)**

17.6   The answer is **D.** The most widely used antimanic agent is lithium. **(p. 356)**

17.7   The answer is **A.** The side effects of lithium are usually mild and transient. **(p. 358)**
        The other answers are false; the correct answers are as follows:
        Anticonvulsants can be used in combination with lithium. **(p. 360)**
        Carbamazepine is an enzyme inducer. **(p. 362)**

17.8   The answer is **C.** The ideal setting for treating patients with secondary mania is the medical-psychiatric unit. **(p. 364)**

17.9   The answer is **D.** DSM-IV criteria for a diagnosis of a manic episode include the symptom of decreased need for sleep. **(p. 348)**

17.10   The answer is **B.** A higher total lifetime number of manic episodes is associated with family history of mood disorder and earlier age at onset. **(p. 349)**

17.11   The answer is **B.** In right-handed persons, risk of depression is associated with left frontotemporal lesions and right parietooccipital lesions. **(p. 351)**

17.12   The answer is **A.** Electroconvulsive therapy is indicated for manic patients who are unresponsive to antimanic agents, at high risk for suicide, or severely manic. **(p. 363)**

Chapter 18

Somatization and Somatoform Disorders

Directions: Select the single best response for each of the following questions:

18.1 All of the following are somatoform disorders **EXCEPT**
   A. Conversion disorder.
   B. Factitious disorder.
   C. Hypochondriasis.
   D. Pain disorder.
   E. Body dysmorphic disorder.

18.2 The tendency to select out and concentrate on weak or infrequent body sensations is one element of
   A. Abnormal illness behavior.
   B. Somatothymia.
   C. Autonomic arousal.
   D. Iatrogenesis.
   E. Somatosensory amplification.

18.3 The percentage of patients with major depression who complain of pain is
   A. <10%.
   B. 20%.
   C. 30%.
   D. 40%.
   E. >50%.

This chapter also corresponds to Chapter 11 in the *Essentials of Consultation-Liaison Psychiatry*.

18.4   Self psychologists theorize that bodily preoccupations can be understood as an attempt to
    A. Restore a sense of integration.
    B. Express hostility.
    C. Gain parental approval.
    D. React to prior sexual abuse.
    E. Assert control over one's environment.

18.5   Which of the following is designed to measure increased sympathetic activity and heightened awareness of bodily functioning?
    A. Minnesota Multiphasic Personality Inventory (MMPI).
    B. West Haven–Yale Multidimensional Pain Inventory (WHYMPI).
    C. State-Trait Anxiety Inventory (STAI).
    D. Modified Somatic Perception Questionnaire (MSPQ).
    E. Millon Clinical Multiaxial Inventory II (MCMI-II).

18.6   The most appropriate management approach for a hostile patient with somatization disorder who denies the importance of psychological or social factors in his or her symptomatology would be to follow
    A. A reattribution approach.
    B. A pharmacological approach.
    C. A confrontation approach.
    D. A directive approach.
    E. A psychotherapeutic approach.

18.7   The most commonly diagnosed somatoform disorder in the general hospital setting is
    A. Undifferentiated somatoform disorder.
    B. Conversion disorder.
    C. Hypochondriasis.
    D. Pain disorder.
    E. Somatoform disorder not otherwise specified.

18.8   According to Barsky's research, the most frequent concurrent Axis I diagnosis in patients with hypochondriasis is
    A. Dysthymia.
    B. Panic disorder.
    C. Generalized anxiety disorder.
    D. Major depression.
    E. Somatization disorder.

18.9   The greatest reduction in pain complaints among patients with somatoform pain is achieved with
   A.   Hypnotherapy.
   B.   Group therapy.
   C.   Exposure therapy.
   D.   Operant treatments.
   E.   Cognitive therapy.

Directions: For each of the statements below, one or more of the answers is correct. Choose

   A.   If 1, 2, and 3 are correct.
   B.   If only 1 and 3 are correct.
   C.   If only 2 and 4 are correct.
   D.   If only 4 is correct.
   E.   If all are correct.

18.10   Factors suggesting a diagnosis of somatization disorder rather than a general medical condition include
   1.   Multiple organ involvement.
   2.   Laboratory abnormalities.
   3.   Onset early in life.
   4.   Short duration of illness.

18.11   The prognosis of conversion disorder depends on
   1.   Acuteness of onset.
   2.   Sociocultural context.
   3.   Personality.
   4.   Symptom pattern.

ANSWERS*

18.1   The answer is **B.** Conversion disorder, hypochondriasis, pain disorder, and body dysmorphic disorder are somatoform disorders. **(p. 370)**

---

*Page numbers within answer sections refer to *The American Psychiatric Press Textbook of Consultation-Liaison Psychiatry.*

18.2   The answer is **E.** The tendency to select out and concentrate on weak or infrequent body sensations is one element of somatosensory amplification. **(p. 371)**

18.3   The answer is **E.** More than 50% of patients with major depression complain of pain. **(p. 375)**

18.4   The answer is **A.** Self psychologists theorize that bodily preoccupations can be understood as an attempt to restore a sense of integration. **(p. 377)**

18.5   The answer is **D.** The Modified Somatic Perception Questionnaire (MSPQ) is designed to measure increased sympathetic activity and heightened awareness of bodily functioning. **(p. 379)**

18.6   The answer is **D.** The most appropriate management approach for a hostile patient with somatization disorder who denies the importance of psychological or social factors in his or her symptomatology would be to follow a directive approach. **(p. 380)**

18.7   The answer is **B.** The most commonly diagnosed somatoform disorder in the general hospital setting is conversion disorder. **(p. 382)**

18.8   The answer is **C.** According to Barsky's research, the most frequent concurrent Axis I diagnosis in patients with hypochondriasis is generalized anxiety disorder. **(p. 386)**

18.9   The answer is **E.** The greatest reduction in pain complaints among patients with somatoform pain is achieved with cognitive therapy. **(p. 394)**

18.10   The answer is **B.** Factors suggesting a diagnosis of somatization disorder rather than a general medical condition include multiple organ involvement and onset early in life. **(p. 384)**

18.11   The answer is **E.** The prognosis of conversion disorder depends on the acuteness of onset, sociocultural context, personality, and symptom pattern. **(p. 388)**

Chapter 19

Anxiety and Panic

Directions: Select the single best response for each of the following questions:

19.1   Pathological anxiety is identical to fear except that its precipitant is
   A.   An interpersonal conflict.
   B.   Substance induced.
   C.   Persistently experienced.
   D.   An unknown intrapsychic conflict.
   E.   The result of a general medical condition.

19.2   In chronic (as opposed to acute) autonomic overactivation, the following predominates:
   A.   Vigilance.
   B.   Palpitations.
   C.   Alarm.
   D.   Panic attacks.
   E.   All of the above.

19.3   A patient whose symptoms include restlessness, fatigue, and irritability, and who is experiencing excessive anxiety plus apprehensive expectation about a number of events or activities, most likely would have a diagnosis of
   A.   Panic disorder.
   B.   Agoraphobia.
   C.   Acute stress disorder.
   D.   Generalized anxiety disorder.
   E.   Social phobia.

This chapter also corresponds to Chapter 12 in the *Essentials of Consultation-Liaison Psychiatry*.

19.4   According to Hall, the majority of medical causes for anxiety are
        A. Circulatory disorders.
        B. Infectious diseases.
        C. Neurological and endocrine disorders.
        D. Rheumatic-collagen-vascular disorders.
        E. Oncological disorders.

19.5   Which of the following is true?
        A. Locus coeruleus ablation increases fearful responses.
        B. Depression and anxiety frequently occur together.
        C. Activation of benzodiazepine receptors results in decreased affinity of
            γ-aminobutyric acid (GABA) to its receptors.
        D. All of the above.
        E. None of the above.

19.6   The stress response was conceptualized as a situation in which the individ-
        ual is confronted with information that produces overwhelming affect,
        which can be most effectively treated through cognitive restructuring, by
        A. Cannon.
        B. Beck.
        C. Horowitz.
        D. Hamilton.
        E. Selye.

19.7   In the consultation-liaison setting, specific phobias
        A. Are very uncommon.
        B. Are likely to be handled by the primary physician.
        C. Are handled by the consultant only if an associated medical condition
            is present.
        D. Are most often revealed by the patient.
        E. Rarely necessitate psychiatric consultation.

19.8   The pharmacological agents most commonly used to manage anxiety are
        the
        A. Hypnotics.
        B. Neuroleptics.
        C. Benzodiazepines.
        D. Barbiturates.
        E. Antidepressants.

Directions: For each of the statements below, one or more of the answers is correct. Choose

    A. If 1, 2, and 3 are correct.
    B. If only 1 and 3 are correct.
    C. If only 2 and 4 are correct.
    D. If only 4 is correct.
    E. If all are correct.

19.9   According to the DSM-IV criteria, the symptoms of a panic attack include
    1. Derealization.
    2. Urinary frequency.
    3. Paresthesias.
    4. Sexual dysfunction.

19.10 Which of the following have been proposed to explain the development of anxiety?
    1. Amygdala stimulation.
    2. Asymmetry of blood flow oxygen utilization.
    3. Reduction in cerebral metabolic rate of glucose in the orbitomedial region.
    4. Extracranial muscle contractions.

19.11 Hall suggests that secondary anxiety can be differentiated from primary anxiety on the basis of its
    1. Duration of more than 2 years.
    2. Presence of other psychiatric symptoms.
    3. Onset between ages 18 and 35.
    4. Absence of recent major psychosocial stressor.

19.12 Hospital environment factors that are associated with the development of anxiety include
    1. Loss of privacy.
    2. Financial burden.
    3. Intrusive medical procedures.
    4. Pain.

19.13   Benzodiazepine agents that have no active metabolites, such as lorazepam, are best suited for patients
1.   With respiratory impairment.
2.   With liver impairment.
3.   Who have a history of substance abuse.
4.   Who are taking multiple medications.

ANSWERS*

19.1   The answer is **D.** Pathological anxiety is identical to fear except that its precipitant is an unknown intrapsychic conflict. **(p. 404)**

19.2   The answer is **A.** In chronic (as opposed to acute) autonomic overactivation, vigilance predominates. **(p. 404)**

19.3   The answer is **D.** A patient whose symptoms include restlessness, fatigue, and irritability, and who is experiencing excessive anxiety plus apprehensive expectation about a number of events or activities, most likely would have a diagnosis of generalized anxiety disorder. **(p. 405)**

19.4   The answer is **C.** According to Hall, the majority of medical causes for anxiety are neurological and endocrine disorders. **(p. 408)**

19.5   The answer is **B.** Depression and anxiety frequently occur together. **(p. 410)**
The other answers are false; the correct answers are as follows:
Locus coeruleus ablation decreases fearful responses. **(p. 410)**
Activation of benzodiazepine receptors results in increased affinity of GABA to its receptors. **(p. 411)**

19.6   The answer is **C.** The stress response was conceptualized as a situation in which the individual is confronted with information that produces overwhelming affect, which can be most effectively treated through cognitive restructuring, by Horowitz. **(pp. 414–415)**

19.7   The answer is **E.** In the consultation-liaison setting, specific phobias rarely necessitate psychiatric consultation. **(p. 415)**

*Page numbers within answer sections refer to *The American Psychiatric Press Textbook of Consultation-Liaison Psychiatry.*

19.8 The answer is **C.** The pharmacological agents most commonly used to manage anxiety are the benzodiazepines. **(p. 418)**

19.9 The answer is **B.** According to the DSM-IV criteria, the symptoms of a panic attack include derealization and paresthesias. **(p. 405)**

19.10 The answer is **A.** Theories to explain the development of anxiety include those pertaining to amygdala stimulation, asymmetry of blood flow oxygen utilization, and reduction in cerebral metabolic rate of glucose in the orbitomedial region. **(p. 412)**

19.11 The answer is **D.** According to Hall, secondary anxiety can be differentiated from primary anxiety on the basis of its absence of recent major psychosocial stressor. **(p. 413)**

19.12 The answer is **E.** Hospital environment factors that are associated with the development of anxiety include loss of privacy, financial burden, intrusive medical procedures, and pain. **(p. 416)**

19.13 The answer is **C.** Benzodiazepine agents that have no active metabolites, such as lorazepam, are best suited for patients with liver impairment and those who are taking multiple medications. **(p. 419)**

Chapter 20

Substance-Related Disorders

Directions: Select the single best response for each of the following questions:

20.1 Which of the following is true?
  A. Psychiatrists are more likely to positively identify alcohol abuse than are gynecologists.
  B. More than 50% of people with an alcohol or drug abuse disorder also have a comorbid psychiatric disorder.
  C. One-quarter of general hospital inpatients have an alcohol-related disorder.
  D. All of the above.
  E. None of the above.

20.2 Alcohol activates
  A. γ-Aminobutyric acid (GABA) chloride ion channels.
  B. N-methyl-D-aspartate (NMDA)-activated ion channels.
  C. N-methyl-D-aspartate (NMDA) receptors.
  D. Serotonin, type 3, receptor–activated ion channels.
  E. All of the above.

20.3 The body metabolizes alcohol at the rate of
  A. 10 mg/kg/hour.
  B. 20 mg/kg/hour.
  C. 50 mg/kg/hour.
  D. 100 mg/kg/hour.
  E. 200 mg/kg/hour.

This chapter also corresponds to Chapter 13 in the *Essentials of Consultation-Liaison Psychiatry*.

20.4   A breath alcohol content (BAC) of greater than 0.4 mg% is associated with
   A.   Euphoria.
   B.   Tolerance.
   C.   Mild coordination problems.
   D.   Ataxia.
   E.   Coma.

20.5   Wernicke-Korsakoff syndrome is also known as
   A.   Alcohol withdrawal syndrome.
   B.   Alcohol-induced persisting amnestic disorder.
   C.   Alcohol-induced psychotic disorder.
   D.   Alcohol withdrawal delirium.
   E.   Chronic alcohol hallucinosis.

20.6   A widely used, 25-question screening test for alcoholism is the
   A.   CAGE screen.
   B.   Michigan Alcohol Screening Test (MAST).
   C.   Structured Clinical Interview for DSM-IV (SCID).
   D.   Alcohol Use Inventory (AUI).
   E.   Addiction Severity Index (ASI).

20.7   Clinical cues to possible opiate abuse or dependence in general hospital
        patients include all of the following **EXCEPT**
   A.   Agitated behavior.
   B.   Decreased globulins.
   C.   Decreased transaminases.
   D.   Pupillary constriction.
   E.   Exaggerated pain complaints.

20.8   Which of the following opioid receptors has selective affinity for heroin,
        meperidine, hydromorphine, and methadone?
   A.   Delta.
   B.   Kappa.
   C.   Lambda.
   D.   Mu.
   E.   Sigma.

20.9   Diazepam is the drug of first choice and is generally required for the management of acute reactions in
   A. Phencyclidine-related disorders.
   B. Amphetamine-related disorders.
   C. Hallucinogen-related disorders.
   D. Cannabis-related disorders.
   E. Inhalant-related disorders.

Directions: For each of the statements below, one or more of the answers is correct. Choose

   A. If 1, 2, and 3 are correct.
   B. If only 1 and 3 are correct.
   C. If only 2 and 4 are correct.
   D. If only 4 is correct.
   E. If all are correct.

20.10   Substance-induced disorders include
   1. Dementia.
   2. Withdrawal.
   3. Delirium.
   4. Dependence.

20.11   Medications that increase blood alcohol levels by inhibiting alcohol dehydrogenase include
   1. Diazepam.
   2. Cimetidine.
   3. Phenytoin.
   4. Chlorpromazine.

20.12   Laboratory findings associated with alcohol abuse include
   1. Decreased mean corpuscular volume (MCV).
   2. Elevated serum glutamic-oxaloacetic transaminase (SGOT).
   3. Increased albumin.
   4. Increased uric acid.

20.13 During the recovery process, the consultation-liaison psychiatrist is responsible for
    1. Providing support.
    2. Confronting the patient about substance-related problems.
    3. Providing access to resources.
    4. Supervising aftercare.

20.14 The most common referral option(s) for patients with alcoholism is to
    1. A psychiatric halfway house.
    2. A specialized treatment program.
    3. A psychiatric inpatient unit.
    4. Alcoholics Anonymous.

20.15 Indications for inpatient treatment of cocaine dependence include
    1. Concurrent serious psychiatric problems.
    2. Chronic freebase use.
    3. Lack of family or other support.
    4. Insufficient motivation for outpatient treatment.

20.16 A well-established association exists between tobacco use and the medical consequence(s) of
    1. Hypertension.
    2. Cirrhosis.
    3. Oral cancers.
    4. Impotence.

ANSWERS*

20.1   The answer is **D.** All of the statements are true. Psychiatrists are more likely to positively identify alcohol abuse than are gynecologists. More than 50% of people with an alcohol or drug abuse disorder also have a comorbid psychiatric disorder. One-quarter of general hospital inpatients have an alcohol-related disorder. **(pp. 429–430)**

20.2   The answer is **A.** Alcohol activates γ-aminobutyric acid (GABA) chloride ion channels. **(p. 431)**

---

*Page numbers within answer sections refer to *The American Psychiatric Press Textbook of Consultation-Liaison Psychiatry.*

20.3   The answer is **D.** The body metabolizes alcohol at the rate of 100 mg/kg/hour. **(p. 431)**

20.4   The answer is **E.** A breath alcohol content (BAC) of greater than 0.4mg% is associated with coma. **(p. 431)**

20.5   The answer is **B.** Wernicke-Korsakoff syndrome is also known as alcohol-induced persisting amnestic disorder. **(p. 432)**

20.6   The answer is **B.** A widely used, 25-question screening test for alcoholism is the Michigan Alcohol Screening Test (MAST). **(p. 438)**

20.7   The answer is **C.** Clinical cues to possible opiate abuse or dependence in general hospital patients include agitated behavior, decreased globulins, pupillary constriction, and exaggerated pain complaints. **(p. 447)**

20.8   The answer is **D.** The mu receptor has selective affinity for heroin, meperidine, hydromorphine, and methadone. **(p. 448)**

20.9   The answer is **A.** Diazepam is the drug of first choice and is generally required for the management of acute reactions in phencyclidine-related disorders. **(p. 456)**

20.10   The answer is **A.** In DSM-IV, substance-induced disorders include dementia, withdrawal, and delirium. **(p. 428)**

20.11   The answer is **C.** Medications that increase blood alcohol levels by inhibiting alcohol dehydrogenase include cimetidine and chlorpromazine. **(p. 435)**

20.12   The answer is **C.** Laboratory findings associated with alcohol abuse include elevated serum glutamic-oxaloacetic transaminase (SGOT) and increased uric acid. **(p. 347)**

20.13   The answer is **A.** During the recovery process, the consultation-liaison psychiatrist is responsible for providing support, confronting the patient about substance-related problems, and providing access to resources. **(pp. 442–443)**

20.14   The answer is **C.** The most common referral options for patients with alcoholism are to a specialized treatment program or to Alcoholics Anonymous. **(p. 444)**

20.15 The answer is **E.** Indications for inpatient treatment of cocaine dependence include concurrent serious psychiatric problems, chronic freebase use, lack of family or other support, and insufficient motivation for outpatient treatment. **(p. 454)**

20.16 The answer is **B.** A well-established association exists between tobacco use and the medical consequences of hypertension and oral cancers. **(p. 458)**

Chapter 21

Sexual Disorders and Dysfunctions

Directions: Select the single best response for each of the following questions:

21.1 After a heart attack, a return to full premorbid level of sexual activity can be anticipated at about
   A. 1–2 weeks.
   B. 2–4 weeks.
   C. 1–2 months.
   D. 2–3 months.
   E. 3–4 months.

21.2 Which of the following is false?
   A. Most impediments to a satisfying sexual life are physiological rather than psychological.
   B. Increased sexual dysfunction after a myocardial infarction is common.
   C. Nongenital tumors can be associated with sexual dysfunction as a direct consequence of treatment.
   D. All of the above.
   E. None of the above.

No corresponding chapter appears in the *Essentials of Consultation-Liaison Psychiatry*.

21.3   Which of the following is true?
   A.   More than half of women with uremia are amenorrheic before meno-
        pause.
   B.   Hypoactive sexual desire disorder is one of the most common psychi-
        atric diagnoses in both men and women with early-stage HIV disease.
   C.   Patients with a diagnosis of end-stage renal disease before adulthood
        are significantly less likely to marry than those given the diagnosis as
        adults.
   D.   All of the above.
   E.   None of the above.

21.4   In multiple sclerosis (MS) patients, sexual dysfunction is often the result of
        which of the following?
   A.   Pharmacotherapy.
   B.   Dysfunction in the lumbosacral spine.
   C.   Low self-esteem.
   D.   Anxiety about sexual performance.
   E.   Depression.

21.5   Paraphilic disorder can be treated most effectively with
   A.   Antiandrogens.
   B.   Estrogens.
   C.   Fluoxetine.
   D.   Neuroleptics.
   E.   All of the above.

Directions: For each of the statements below, one or more of the answers is
correct. Choose

   A.   If 1, 2, and 3 are correct.
   B.   If only 1 and 3 are correct.
   C.   If only 2 and 4 are correct.
   D.   If only 4 is correct.
   E.   If all are correct.

21.6   Factors that can contribute to impotence in patients with diabetes mellitus
        include
   1.   Hormonal.
   2.   Neuropathic.
   3.   Vascular.
   4.   Psychological.

21.7   The following medication(s) can cause increased libido
        1. Diazepam.
        2. Steroids.
        3. Methadone.
        4. Estrogens.

21.8   The following medication(s) can cause impotence
        1. Carbamazepine.
        2. Clozapine.
        3. Lithium.
        4. Trazodone.

21.9   Problems related to hypersexuality can lead to hospital admission in pa-
        tients with
        1. Huntington's chorea.
        2. Parkinson's disease.
        3. Klüver-Bucy syndrome.
        4. Malingering.

ANSWERS*

21.1   The answer is **D.** After a heart attack, a return to full premorbid level of sex-
        ual activity can be anticipated at about 2–3 months. **(p. 469)**

21.2   The answer is **A.** Most impediments to a satisfying sexual life are psycho-
        logical rather than physiological. **(pp. 468–469)**

21.3   The answer is **D.** More than half of women with uremia are amenorrheic
        before menopause. Hypoactive sexual desire disorder is one of the most
        common psychiatric diagnoses in both men and women with early-stage
        HIV disease. Patients with a diagnosis of end-stage renal disease before
        adulthood are significantly less likely to marry than those given the diag-
        nosis as adults. **(pp. 470–471)**

21.4   The answer is **B.** Dysfunction in the lumbosacral spine accounts for many
        of the sexual difficulties experienced by patients with multiple sclerosis
        (MS). **(p. 477)**

21.5   The answer is **A.** Paraphilic disorder can be treated most effectively with antiandrogens. **(p. 481)**

21.6   The answer is **E.** Factors that can contribute to impotence in patients with diabetes mellitus include hormonal, neuropathic, vascular, and psychological factors. **(p. 471)**

21.7   The answer is **C.** Medications that can cause increased libido include steroids and estrogens. **(pp. 473–475)**

21.8   The answer is **B.** Medications that can cause impotence include carbamazepine and lithium. **(pp. 473–475)**

21.9   The answer is **B.** Problems related to hypersexuality can lead to hospital admission in patients with Huntington's chorea and Klüver-Bucy syndrome. **(p. 478)**

Chapter 22

Eating Disorders

Directions: Select the single best response for each of the following questions:

22.1 Anorexia begins most often in females between ages
    A. 7 and 12 years.
    B. 13 and 18 years.
    C. 19 and 24 years.
    D. 25 and 30 years.
    E. 30 years and older.

22.2 Which of the following is true?
    A. Bulimia has the highest mortality of all psychiatric disorders.
    B. During terminal starvation, insulin is released, which interferes with the cell's ability to use energy.
    C. Only 20% of bulimic eating binges are planned.
    D. All of the above.
    E. None of the above.

22.3 During the refeeding phase of treatment for anorexia, dyspnea can be associated with
    A. Decreased myocardial demand.
    B. ST segment depression on the electrocardiogram (ECG).
    C. Elevated venous pressure.
    D. Premature ventricular contractions.
    E. Widening of the QRS interval on the electrocardiogram (ECG).

This chapter also corresponds to Chapter 14 in the *Essentials of Consultation-Liaison Psychiatry.*

22.4   Which of the following is false?

   A.   The pharmacotherapy for anorexia is more effective than that for bulimia.
   B.   Serotonin levels are lower in bulimic-anorexic patients than in purely restrictive anorexic patients.
   C.   Most anorexic patients need antidepressant drug therapy.
   D.   All of the above.
   E.   None of the above.

Directions: For each of the statements below, one or more of the answers is correct. Choose

   A.   If 1, 2, and 3 are correct.
   B.   If only 1 and 3 are correct.
   C.   If only 2 and 4 are correct.
   D.   If only 4 is correct.
   E.   If all are correct.

22.5   Predisposing factors of anorexic patients often include
   1.   History of sexual abuse.
   2.   Mildly overweight.
   3.   Recent stressful life situation.
   4.   High intelligence.

22.6   Frequent medical complications of anorexia include
   1.   Hypokalemia.
   2.   Leukopenia.
   3.   Cardiac arrhythmia.
   4.   Paralysis.

22.7   The euthyroid sick syndrome includes which of the following symptoms?
   1.   Bradycardia.
   2.   Heat intolerance.
   3.   Constipation.
   4.   Hypocholesterolemia.

22.8   Psychotherapeutic issues of importance to anorexic patients include
   1.   Overcoming fears about normal body size.
   2.   Improving self-esteem.
   3.   Redefining interpersonal relationships.
   4.   Developing assertiveness.

22.9 Pharmacotherapy most commonly used by eating disorder specialists for bulimic patients includes
1. Thioridazine.
2. Imipramine.
3. Cyproheptadine.
4. Fluoxetine.

ANSWERS*

22.1 The answer is **B.** Anorexia begins most often in females between ages 13 and 18 years. **(p. 488)**

22.2 The answer is **E.** All of the answers are false; correct answers are as follows: Anorexia has the highest mortality of all psychiatric disorders. **(p. 489)** During terminal starvation, cachetin is released, which interferes with the cell's ability to use energy. **(p. 490)** Eighty percent of bulimic eating binges are planned. **(p. 491)**

22.3 The answer is **C.** During the refeeding phase of treatment for anorexia, dyspnea can be associated with elevated venous pressure. **(p. 495)**

22.4 The answer is **A.** The pharmacotherapy for bulimia is more effective than that for anorexia. **(pp. 499–500)**

22.5 The answer is **E.** Predisposing factors of anorexic patients often include a history of sexual abuse, mildly overweight, a recent stressful life situation, and high intelligence. **(p. 489)**

22.6 The answer is **A.** Frequent medical complications of anorexia include hypokalemia, leukopenia, and cardiac arrhythmia. **(p. 493)**

22.7 The answer is **B.** The euthyroid sick syndrome includes bradycardia and constipation. **(p. 496)**

---

*Page numbers within answer sections refer to *The American Psychiatric Press Textbook of Consultation-Liaison Psychiatry*.

22.8   The answer is **E.** Psychotherapeutic issues of importance to anorexic pa-
        tients include overcoming fears about normal body size, improving
        self-esteem, redefining interpersonal relationships, and developing asser-
        tiveness. **(p. 499)**

22.9   The answer is **C.** Pharmacotherapy most commonly used by eating disor-
        der specialists for bulimic patients includes imipramine and fluoxetine. **(p.
        500)**

Chapter 23

Sleep Disorders

QUESTIONS

Directions: Select the single best response for each of the following questions:

23.1 Delta sleep consists of
   A. Stages 1 and 2 of non–rapid eye movement (NREM) sleep.
   B. Stages 2 and 3 of non–rapid eye movement (NREM) sleep.
   C. Stages 3 and 4 of non–rapid eye movement (NREM) sleep.
   D. Stage 2 of non–rapid eye movement (NREM) sleep.
   E. Rapid eye movement (REM) sleep.

23.2 The rhythmic alteration of non–rapid eye movement (NREM) and rapid eye movement (REM) sleep has a cycle length of about
   A. 20 minutes.
   B. 30 minutes.
   C. 50 minutes.
   D. 70 minutes.
   E. 90 minutes.

23.3 Sleep-related epilepsy is classified by the International Classification of Sleep Disorders as
   A. A parasomnia.
   B. A medical-psychiatric sleep disorder.
   C. A circadian rhythm sleep disorder.
   D. An extrinsic sleep disorder.
   E. An intrinsic sleep disorder.

This chapter also corresponds to Chapter 15 in the *Essentials of Consultation-Liaison Psychiatry.*

23.4   Among patients referred for psychiatric consultation in the general hospital setting, the most common type of insomnia is
     A.   Transient insomnia.
     B.   Chronic insomnia.
     C.   Hypersomnia.
     D.   Parasomnia.
     E.   Sleep disorder due to a general medical condition.

23.5   The mainstay of drug treatment for insomnia in hospitalized patients is
     A.   Barbiturates.
     B.   Benzodiazepines.
     C.   Neuroleptics.
     D.   Sedating antihistamines.
     E.   Sedating antidepressants.

23.6   The Multiple Sleep Latency Test (MSLT) is the gold standard for evaluation of
     A.   Sleep apnea.
     B.   Periodic leg movements of sleep (PLMS).
     C.   Excessive daytime somnolence (EDS).
     D.   Restless legs syndrome (RLS).
     E.   Circadian rhythm sleep disorder.

23.7   Convulsive seizures are generally equally distributed between waking and sleep in patients with
     A.   Partial epilepsy.
     B.   Morpheic epilepsy.
     C.   Rolandic epilepsy.
     D.   Generalized epilepsy.
     E.   All of the above.

Directions: For each of the statements below, one or more of the answers is correct. Choose

     A.   If 1, 2, and 3 are correct.
     B.   If only 1 and 3 are correct.
     C.   If only 2 and 4 are correct.
     D.   If only 4 is correct.
     E.   If all are correct.

23.8 Patients with which of the following conditions can develop significant worsening of ventricular arrhythmias during sleep?
1. Chronic obstructive pulmonary disease.
2. Alveolary hypoventilation.
3. Sleep apnea.
4. Alzheimer's dementia.

23.9 Which of the following is classified in DSM-IV as a parasomnia?
1. Narcolepsy.
2. Breathing-related sleep disorder.
3. Hypersomnia.
4. Sleepwalking disorder.

23.10 A consultant's goal(s) in managing a hospitalized patient's sleep disruption should be to
1. Increase the patient's non–rapid eye movement (NREM) sleep.
2. Prescribe hypnotics.
3. Make sure the patient gets 8 hours of sleep within a 24-hour period.
4. Restore sleep to the patient's prehospitalization baseline.

23.11 Causes of excessive daytime somnolence include
1. Sleep apnea.
2. Restless legs syndrome.
3. Idiopathic central nervous system hypersomnia.
4. Narcolepsy.

23.12 Signs and symptoms of obstructive sleep apnea syndrome include
1. Excessive daytime somnolence.
2. Dry mouth.
3. Arrhythmias.
4. Periodic leg movements.

23.13 In Parkinson's disease, sleep disturbance is commonly caused by
1. Antiparkinsonian medications.
2. Interstitial discharges.
3. Disordered breathing due to interference with respiratory muscles.
4. Gastroesophageal reflux.

ANSWERS*

23.1   The answer is **C.** Delta sleep consists of stages 3 and 4 of non–rapid eye movement (NREM) sleep. **(p. 507)**

23.2   The answer is **E.** The rhythmic alteration of non–rapid eye movement (NREM) and rapid eye movement (REM) sleep has a cycle length of about 90 minutes. **(p. 507)**

23.3   The answer is **B.** Sleep-related epilepsy is classified by the International Classification of Sleep Disorders as a medical-psychiatric sleep disorder. **(p. 509)**

23.4   The answer is **A.** Among patients referred for psychiatric consultation in the general hospital setting, more than 70% can be expected to have transient insomnia. **(p. 512)**

23.5   The answer is **B.** The mainstay of drug treatment for insomnia in hospitalized patients is benzodiazepines. **(pp. 517–518)**

23.6   The answer is **C.** The Multiple Sleep Latency Test (MSLT) is the gold standard for evaluation of excessive daytime somnolence (EDS). **(p. 520)**

23.7   The answer is **D.** Convulsive seizures are generally equally distributed between waking and sleep in patients with generalized epilepsy. **(pp. 524–525)**

23.8   The answer is **A.** Patients with chronic obstructive pulmonary disease, alveolary hypoventilation, and sleep apnea can develop significant worsening of ventricular arrhythmias during sleep. **(p. 523)**

23.9   The answer is **D.** Sleepwalking disorder is classified in DSM-IV as a parasomnia. **(p. 508)**

23.10   The answer is **D.** A consultant's goal(s) in managing a hospitalized patient's sleep disruption should be to restore sleep to the patient's prehospitalization baseline. **(p. 508)**

---

*Page numbers within answer sections refer to *The American Psychiatric Press Textbook of Consultation-Liaison Psychiatry.*

23.11　The answer is **E.** Causes of excessive daytime somnolence include sleep apnea, restless legs syndrome, idiopathic central nervous system hypersomnia, and narcolepsy. **(p. 520)**

23.12　The answer is **A.** Signs and symptoms of obstructive sleep apnea syndrome include excessive daytime somnolence, dry mouth, and arrhythmias. **(p. 521)**

23.13　The answer is **B.** In Parkinson's disease, sleep disturbance is commonly caused by antiparkinsonian medications and disordered breathing due to interference with respiratory muscles. **(p. 526)**

Chapter 24

Factitious Disorders and Malingering

Directions: Select the single best response for each of the following questions:

24.1 The mind "uses" the body to control negative impulses in
   A. Malingering.
   B. Factitious disorder by proxy.
   C. Munchausen syndrome.
   D. Conversion disorder.
   E. Depressive disorder due to a general medical condition.

24.2 A factitious disorder with predominantly psychological symptoms is
   A. Munchausen syndrome.
   B. Ganser's syndrome.
   C. Pseudologia phantastica.
   D. Unconscious feigning.
   E. Factitious disorder by proxy.

24.3 Which of the following is true?
   A. Factitious disorders are benign conditions.
   B. It is not uncommon for factitious disorder patients to sue their doctors.
   C. A patient suspected of malingering should be confronted with a direct accusation.
   D. All of the above.
   E. None of the above.

This chapter also corresponds to Chapter 16 in the *Essentials of Consultation-Liaison Psychiatry.*

24.4   The category of malingering most frequently seen by consultation-liaison
        psychiatrists is
        A. Simulation of an illness.
        B. Exacerbation of a previous illness.
        C. Deliberate embellishment of previous or concurrent illness.
        D. Malingering by proxy.
        E. Pseudomalingering.

24.5   The most valuable diagnostic instrument among those listed below for
        identifying malingering patients is
        A. Symptom Checklist—90.
        B. Beck Depression Inventory (BDI).
        C. General Health Questionnaire.
        D. Structured Clinical Interview for DSM-IV (SCID).
        E. Minnesota Multiphasic Personality Inventory—2 (MMPI-2).

Directions: For each of the statements below, one or more of the answers is
correct. Choose

        A. If 1, 2, and 3 are correct.
        B. If only 1 and 3 are correct.
        C. If only 2 and 4 are correct.
        D. If only 4 is correct.
        E. If all are correct.

24.6   Factitious disorder patients with Munchausen syndrome are most likely to
        be
        1. Elderly women, often widowed.
        2. Elderly men, often widowed.
        3. Women ages 20–40, who work in medical professions.
        4. Middle-aged men, usually unmarried.

24.7   Diseases or conditions more commonly associated with factitious behav-
        ior include
        1. Kidney stones.
        2. Epilepsy.
        3. Cancer.
        4. Alzheimer's disease.

■ ANSWERS*

24.1   The answer is **D.** The mind "uses" the body to control negative impulses in conversion disorder. **(p. 534)**

24.2   The answer is **B.** A factitious disorder with predominantly psychological symptoms is Ganser's syndrome. **(p. 537)**

24.3   The answer is **B.** It is not uncommon for factitious disorder patients to sue their doctors. **(p. 539)**
    The other answers are false; the correct answers are as follows:
    Factitious disorders are not benign conditions; they are associated with considerable morbidity and even mortality. **(p. 540)**
    A patient suspected of malingering should be confronted with a subtle communication that indicates the doctor is aware of the manipulation. **(p. 542)**

24.4   The answer is **C.** The category of malingering most frequently seen by consultation-liaison psychiatrists is deliberate embellishment of previous or concurrent illness. **(pp. 540–541)**

24.5   The answer is **E.** Among those listed, the most valuable diagnostic instrument for identifying malingering patients is the Minnesota Multiphasic Personality Inventory—2 (MMPI-2). **(p. 541)**

24.6   The answer is **D.** Factitious disorder patients with Munchausen syndrome tend to be middle-aged men, usually unmarried. **(p. 535)**

24.7   The answer is **A.** Diseases or conditions more commonly associated with factitious behavior include kidney stones, epilepsy, and cancer. **(p. 535)**

---

*Page numbers within answer sections refer to *The American Psychiatric Press Textbook of Consultation-Liaison Psychiatry.*

Section III

Clinical
Consultation-Liaison
Settings

Chapter 25

Internal Medicine and Medical Subspecialties

Directions: Select the single best response for each of the following questions:

25.1   Among the following, which is the most reliable inducer of arrhythmias in susceptible patients?
    A.   Carotid sinus massage.
    B.   Valsalva maneuver.
    C.   Discussion about illness and death.
    D.   Hyperventilation.
    E.   Dive reflex activation.

25.2   Among the following interventions, the greatest reduction in myocardial infarction recurrence and cardiac death has been shown with
    A.   Group psychotherapy.
    B.   Thrombolytic therapy.
    C.   β-Blockers.
    D.   Tricyclic antidepressants.
    E.   Surgery.

This chapter also corresponds to Chapter 17 in the *Essentials of Consultation-Liaison Psychiatry.*

25.3   Which of the following is true?
A. Tricyclic antidepressants may be proarrhythmic.
B. Tricyclic antidepressants do not adversely affect left ventricular function.
C. Early somatic treatment is recommended post–myocardial infarction for severely depressed patients.
D. All of the above.
E. None of the above.

25.4   Hospitalized cardiac patients with acute anxiety are most commonly treated with
A. Lithium.
B. Trazodone.
C. Selective serotonin reuptake inhibitors.
D. Benzodiazepines.
E. Electroconvulsive therapy (ECT).

25.5   Men are more likely than women to experience
A. Irritable bowel syndrome.
B. Constipation.
C. Postprandial bloating.
D. Functional biliary pain.
E. None of the above.

25.6   The percentage of patients with bowel disturbances who seek medical consultation for their symptoms is approximately
A. 40%.
B. 50%.
C. 60%.
D. 70%.
E. 80%.

25.7   Patients who have an esophageal motility disorder are most likely to also have
A. Social phobia.
B. Panic disorder.
C. Somatization disorder.
D. Substance abuse disorder.
E. Major depression.

25.8 According to Lydiard's research, patients who have irritable bowel syndrome are most likely to have a lifetime history of
A. Social phobia.
B. Panic disorder.
C. Somatization disorder.
D. Substance abuse disorder.
E. Major depression.

25.9 Patients with irritable bowel syndrome who have no significant psychopathology
A. Should not be treated with antidepressants.
B. Should be treated with antipsychotics.
C. Should be treated with antihistamines.
D. Can be treated with high-dose antidepressants or antianxiety agents if they are treatment-refractory.
E. Can be treated with low-dose antidepressants or antianxiety agents if they are treatment-refractory.

25.10 Which of the following is false?
A. Franz Alexander's specificity theory incorrectly assumed that inflammatory bowel disease is an "organic neurosis."
B. Severity of inflammatory bowel disease is associated with the presence or absence of psychiatric illness.
C. Receiving support from a patient advocacy group can greatly enhance the coping ability of inflammatory bowel disease patients.
D. All of the above.
E. None of the above.

25.11 Among the following medical conditions, major depression is most likely to be seen in patients with
A. Diabetes mellitus.
B. Hypothyroidism.
C. Hyperthyroidism.
D. Cushing's syndrome.
E. Addison's disease.

25.12 A consultant should be aware that the greatest concern in a patient with hypothyroidism is
   A. Panic attacks.
   B. Mania.
   C. Cognitive deficits.
   D. Substance abuse.
   E. Anxiety.

25.13 Autoantibodies to ribosomal P protein have been associated with the psychiatric manifestations of
   A. Systemic lupus erythematosus.
   B. Pheochromocytoma.
   C. Acromegaly.
   D. Cobalamin deficiency.
   E. None of the above.

25.14 A specific treatment for chronic fatigue syndrome is
   A. Amitriptyline with naproxen.
   B. Amitriptyline without naproxen.
   C. Cyclobenzaprine.
   D. Vitamin B_{12}.
   E. None of the above.

Directions: For each of the statements below, one or more of the answers is correct. Choose

   A. If 1, 2, and 3 are correct.
   B. If only 1 and 3 are correct.
   C. If only 2 and 4 are correct.
   D. If only 4 is correct.
   E. If all are correct.

25.15 In patients with cardiac disease, denial of cardiac symptoms can result in
   1. Reduced anxiety.
   2. Decreased catecholamine release.
   3. Better in-hospital clinical course.
   4. Increased compliance.

25.16 The patient's perception of severity of dyspnea correlates with
    1. Tendency to hyperventilate.
    2. Fear of dyspnea.
    3. Catastrophic cognition.
    4. Intrapsychic meaning of the symptom.

25.17 When compared with nondepressed patients, depressed patients manifest
    1. Lower respiratory rates.
    2. Elevated resting end tidal volumes.
    3. Elevated levels of pCO_2.
    4. Decreased CO_2 retention.

25.18 Clinically, nicotine has been shown to
    1. Decrease heart rate.
    2. Act as an acute stimulus for breathing.
    3. Decrease blood pressure.
    4. Increase dopamine release in the prefrontal cortex.

25.19 Renal transplantation is contraindicated in patients who have
    1. Irreversible psychosis.
    2. Major depression.
    3. Dementia.
    4. Delirium.

25.20 Dialysis dementia is characterized by
    1. Depression.
    2. Progressive encephalopathy.
    3. Impaired memory.
    4. Normal speech.

ANSWERS*

25.1 The answer is **C.** Discussion about illness and death is a more reliable inducer of arrhythmias than are physical maneuvers in susceptible patients. **(p. 551)**

---

*Page numbers within answer sections refer to *The American Psychiatric Press Textbook of Consultation-Liaison Psychiatry.*

25.2   The answer is **A.** Greater reduction in myocardial infarction recurrence and cardiac death has been shown with group psychotherapy than with any medical or surgical interventions. **(p. 554)**

25.3   The answer is **D.** All of the statements are true. Tricyclic antidepressants may be proarrhythmic. Tricyclic antidepressants do not adversely affect left ventricular function. Early somatic treatment is recommended post–myocardial infarction for severely depressed patients. **(pp. 557–558)**

25.4   The answer is **D.** Hospitalized cardiac patients with acute anxiety are most commonly treated with benzodiazepines. **(p. 559)**

25.5   The answer is **C.** Men are more likely than women to experience postprandial bloating. **(p. 567)**

25.6   The answer is **B.** Approximately 50% of patients with bowel disturbances seek medical consultation for their symptoms. **(p. 568)**

25.7   The answer is **E.** Patients who have an esophageal motility disorder are most likely to also have major depression. **(p. 569)**

25.8   The answer is **E.** According to Lydiard's research, patients who have irritable bowel syndrome are most likely to have a lifetime history of major depression. **(p. 570)**

25.9   The answer is **E.** Patients with irritable bowel syndrome who have no significant psychopathology can be treated with low-dose antidepressants or antianxiety agents if they are treatment-refractory. **(p. 571)**

25.10   The answer is **B.** Severity of inflammatory bowel disease is not associated with the presence or absence of psychiatric illness. **(pp. 571–572)**

25.11   The answer is **D.** Among the following medical conditions, major depression is most likely to be seen in patients with Cushing's syndrome. **(p. 580)**

25.12   The answer is **C.** A consultant should be aware that the greatest concern in a patient with hypothyroidism is cognitive deficits. **(p. 580)**

25.13   The answer is **A.** Autoantibodies to ribosomal P protein have been associated with the psychiatric manifestations of systemic lupus erythematosus. **(p. 585)**

25.14 The answer is **E.** No specific treatment currently exists for chronic fatigue syndrome. **(p. 591)**

25.15 The answer is **A.** In patients with cardiac disease, denial of cardiac symptoms can result in reduced anxiety, decreased catecholamine release, and better in-hospital clinical course. **(p. 555)**

25.16 The answer is **E.** The patient's perception of severity of dyspnea correlates with the patient's tendency to hyperventilate, fear of dyspnea, catastrophic cognition, and intrapsychic meaning of the symptom. **(p. 561)**

25.17 The answer is **B.** When compared with nondepressed patients, depressed patients manifest lower respiratory rates and elevated levels of pCO_2. **(p. 562)**

25.18 The answer is **C.** Clinically, nicotine has been shown to act as an acute stimulus for breathing and to increase dopamine release in the prefrontal cortex. **(p. 564)**

25.19 The answer is **B.** Renal transplantation is contraindicated in patients who have irreversible psychosis or dementia. **(p. 574)**

25.20 The answer is **A.** Dialysis dementia is characterized by depression, progressive encephalopathy, and impaired memory. **(p. 577)**

Chapter 26

Surgery and Surgical Subspecialties

Directions: Select the single best response for each of the following questions:

26.1   Preoperative panic or surgery refusal occurs in what percentage of general surgery patients?
   A.   5%.
   B.   10%.
   C.   15%.
   D.   20%.
   E.   25%.

26.2   Which of the following is true?
   A.   Psychiatrists can determine a patient's legal competency to make medical decisions.
   B.   The civil commitment process of the state can be used to warrant neuropsychiatric evaluation against a protesting patient's will.
   C.   The psychiatrist must document the pertinent aspects of a patient's mental status examination after a surgeon and psychiatrist have agreed to pursue judicial review of the patient's competency.
   D.   All of the above.
   E.   None of the above.

This chapter also corresponds to Chapter 18 in the *Essentials of Consultation-Liaison Psychiatry.*

26.3   The mental disorder most frequently diagnosed postoperatively in surgical
       patients is
       A. Anxiety.
       B. Posttraumatic stress disorder (PTSD).
       C. Delirium.
       D. Mania.
       E. Depression.

26.4   Preoperative psychiatric consultation for patients with cardiac assist de-
       vices is generally focused primarily on
       A. Pain control.
       B. Reduction of anxiety.
       C. Reduction of bleeding.
       D. Support of family members.
       E. None of the above.

26.5   Anxiety experienced during ventilator weaning perioperatively is caused by
       A. Delirium.
       B. Dyspnea.
       C. Inadequate pain control.
       D. Overmedication.
       E. Postcardiotomy delirium.

26.6   In the orthopedic surgery setting, psychiatric consultants who work with
       patients with borderline personality disorder should actively promote a
       behavioral management program that includes all of the following
       EXCEPT
       A. Understanding the patient's need for constant attention from hospital
           staff.
       B. Assisting the staff in diminishing the patient's fears.
       C. Confronting the patient's defenses.
       D. Setting firm limits on the patient's dependency and rage.
       E. Communicating clearly with the patient and staff.

26.7   Tunnel vision is a functional form of vision loss that is sometimes observed
       in patients with
       A. Palinopsia.
       B. End-stage glaucoma.
       C. Conversion disorder.
       D. Mania.
       E. Schizophrenia.

26.8 During the first 24–72 hours following a severe burn, most patients experience
   A. Delirium.
   B. Denial.
   C. Depression.
   D. Posttraumatic stress disorder (PTSD).
   E. Lucidity.

Directions: For each of the statements below, one or more of the answers is correct. Choose

   A. If 1, 2, and 3 are correct.
   B. If only 1 and 3 are correct.
   C. If only 2 and 4 are correct.
   D. If only 4 is correct.
   E. If all are correct.

26.9 According to Hackett and Weisman (1960), psychiatric complications termed *operative syndromes* include
   1. Addiction.
   2. Suicidal depression.
   3. Disruptive ward behavior.
   4. Acute psychosis.

26.10 Congenital cardiovascular conditions that often necessitate cardiovascular surgery include
   1. Mitral stenosis.
   2. Bicuspid mitral valve.
   3. Ventricular fibrillation.
   4. Pulmonic stenosis.

26.11 The factors that determine a patient's risk of developing postcardiotomy delirium include
   1. Cardiac status.
   2. Severity of illness.
   3. Complexity of surgical procedure.
   4. Preoperative organic brain disease.

26.12   Topical β-blockers used to treat glaucoma can cause
    1.   Depression.
    2.   Mania.
    3.   Hallucinations.
    4.   Blindness.

26.13   Early postoperative interventions for anxiety in disfigured patients include
    1.   Desensitization.
    2.   Pharmacological therapy.
    3.   Cognitive restructuring.
    4.   Group therapy.

ANSWERS*

26.1   The answer is **A.** Preoperative panic or surgery refusal occurs in 5% of general surgery patients. **(p. 611)**

26.2   The answer is **B.** In rare instances, the civil commitment process of the state can be used to warrant neuropsychiatric evaluation against a protesting patient's will. **(p. 614)**
The other answers are false; the correct answers are as follows:
A judge, not a psychiatrist, determines a patient's legal competency to make medical decisions. **(p. 612)**
The psychiatrist must document the pertinent aspects of a patient's mental status examination before a surgeon and psychiatrist have agreed to pursue judicial review of a patient's competency. **(p. 612)**

26.3   The answer is **C.** The mental disorder most frequently diagnosed postoperatively in surgical patients is delirium. **(p. 614)**

26.4   The answer is **D.** Preoperative psychiatric consultation for patients with cardiac assist devices is generally focused primarily on support of family members. **(p. 619)**

26.5   The answer is **B.** Anxiety experienced during ventilator weaning perioperatively is caused by dyspnea. **(p. 620)**

---

*Page numbers within answer sections refer to *The American Psychiatric Press Textbook of Consultation-Liaison Psychiatry.*

26.6 The answer is **C.** In the orthopedic surgery setting, psychiatric consultants who work with patients with borderline personality disorder should actively promote a behavioral management program that includes understanding the patient's need for constant attention from hospital staff, assisting the staff in diminishing the patient's fears, setting firm limits on the patient's dependency and rage, and communicating clearly with the patient and staff. **(p. 624)**

26.7 The answer is **C.** Tunnel vision is a functional form of vision loss that is sometimes observed in patients with conversion disorder. **(p. 626)**

26.8 The answer is **E.** During the first 24–72 hours following a severe burn, most patients experience a period of initial lucidity. **(p. 627)**

26.9 The answer is **E.** According to Hackett and Weisman (1960), psychiatric complications termed *operative syndromes* include addiction, suicidal depression, disruptive ward behavior, and acute psychosis. **(p. 609)**

26.10 The answer is **C.** Congenital cardiovascular conditions that often necessitate cardiovascular surgery include bicuspid mitral valve and pulmonic stenosis. **(p. 617)**

26.11 The answer is **E.** The factors that determine a patient's risk of developing postcardiotomy delirium include cardiac status, severity of illness, complexity of surgical procedure, and preoperative organic brain disease. **(p. 619)**

26.12 The answer is **B.** Topical β-blockers used to treat glaucoma can cause depression and hallucinations. **(p. 626)**

26.13 The answer is **A.** Early postoperative interventions for anxiety in disfigured patients include desensitization, pharmacological therapy, and cognitive restructuring. **(p. 631)**

Chapter 27

Transplantation

Directions: Select the single best response for each of the following questions:

27.1   After a transplant patient has undergone a general screening by the organ specialist, the patient's entry into the formal assessment phase is usually facilitated by the
A.   Psychiatrist.
B.   Organ transplant psychiatry specialist.
C.   Primary care physician.
D.   Nursing coordinator.
E.   Social worker.

27.2   Among the following instruments, which includes ratings for the affective and mental states of transplant candidates?
A.   Beck Depression Inventory (BDI).
B.   Transplantation Evaluation Rating Scale (TERS).
C.   Minnesota Multiphasic Personality Inventory—2 (MMPI-2).
D.   Psychosocial Assessment of Candidates for Transplant (PACT).
E.   Thematic Apperception Test (TAT).

This chapter also corresponds to Chapter 19 in the *Essentials of Consultation-Liaison Psychiatry*.

27.3   The most common psychiatric disorder in patients with liver disease in the weeks before and after transplantation is
      A.   Major depression.
      B.   Panic disorder.
      C.   Adjustment disorder.
      D.   Substance abuse disorder.
      E.   Delirium.

27.4   Which of the following is false?
      A.   Adult transplant recipients have fewer compliance difficulties than do children receiving transplants.
      B.   Prior compliance history reliably predicts posttransplant compliance.
      C.   Lower socioeconomic class is associated with increased risk for non-compliance in transplant patients.
      D.   All of the above.
      E.   None of the above.

27.5   A profoundly fatigued transplant patient could benefit from therapy with
      A.   Methylphenidate.
      B.   Valproate.
      C.   Clozapine.
      D.   Trazodone.
      E.   All of the above.

27.6   Which of the following is true?
      A.   Transplant recipients have greater anxiety 4–12 months posttransplant than they have at the time of posttransplant discharge.
      B.   Most transplant recipients return to work or other pretransplant roles within 1 year.
      C.   Gross tremor is a common problem in organ transplant recipients.
      D.   All of the above.
      E.   None of the above.

Directions: For each of the statements below, one or more of the answers is correct. Choose

      A.   If 1, 2, and 3 are correct.
      B.   If only 1 and 3 are correct.
      C.   If only 2 and 4 are correct.
      D.   If only 4 is correct.
      E.   If all are correct.

27.7   Absolute contraindications to solid organ transplantation include
1. Active substance abuse.
2. Dementia.
3. Psychosis significantly limiting consent.
4. Life-threatening mood disorder.

27.8   Neuropsychiatric syndromes associated with cyclosporine toxicity include
1. Cortical blindness.
2. Frontal-lobe syndromes.
3. Delirium.
4. Dementia-like syndromes.

27.9   Liver transplant recipients can experience seizures resulting from treatment with
1. Benzodiazepines.
2. Corticosteroids.
3. Haloperidol.
4. Cyclosporine.

ANSWERS*

27.1   The answer is **D.** After a transplant patient has undergone a general screening by the organ specialist, the patient's entry into the formal assessment phase is usually facilitated by the nursing coordinator. **(p. 643)**

27.2   The answer is **B.** The Transplantation Evaluation Rating Scale (TERS) includes ratings for the affective and mental states of transplant candidates. **(p. 645)**

27.3   The answer is **E.** The most common psychiatric disorder in patients with liver disease in the weeks before and after transplantation is delirium. **(p. 646)**

---

*Page numbers within answer sections refer to *The American Psychiatric Press Textbook of Consultation-Liaison Psychiatry.*

27.4   The answer is **E.** All of the statements are true. Adult transplant recipients have fewer compliance difficulties than do children receiving transplants. Prior compliance history reliably predicts posttransplant compliance. Lower socioeconomic class is associated with increased risk for noncompliance in transplant patients. **(p. 649)**

27.5   The answer is **A.** A profoundly fatigued transplant patient could benefit from therapy with methylphenidate. **(p. 652)**

27.6   The answer is **D.** All of the statements are true. Transplant recipients have greater anxiety 4–12 months posttransplant than they have at the time of posttransplant discharge. Most transplant recipients return to work or other pretransplant roles within 1 year. Gross tremor is a common problem in organ transplant recipients. **(pp. 660–663)**

27.7   The answer is **B.** Absolute contraindications to solid organ transplantation include active substance abuse and psychosis significantly limiting consent. **(p. 644)**

27.8   The answer is **E.** Neuropsychiatric syndromes associated with cyclosporine toxicity include cortical blindness, frontal-lobe syndromes, delirium, and dementia-like syndromes. **(p. 658)**

27.9   The answer is **D.** Liver transplant recipients can experience seizures resulting from treatment with cyclosporine. **(p. 659)**

Chapter 28

Oncology

Directions: Select the single best response for each of the following questions:

28.1   Nausea and vomiting in anticipation of chemotherapy can be treated effectively with
   A.   Alprazolam with dexamethasone and perphenazine.
   B.   Ondansetron with dexamethasone and lorazepam.
   C.   Ganciclovir with perphenazine and lorazepam.
   D.   Ganciclovir with dexamethasone and lorazepam.
   E.   Perphenazine with ganciclovir and alprazolam.

28.2   A disproportionately high incidence of dysphoria is associated with
   A.   Head and neck cancer.
   B.   Breast cancer.
   C.   Prostate cancer.
   D.   Pancreatic cancer.
   E.   Hodgkin's disease.

28.3   Among the following anticancer medications, the one most commonly associated with affective instability is
   A.   Procarbazine.
   B.   Tamoxifen.
   C.   Methotrexate.
   D.   Granisetron.
   E.   Interferon.

_____

This chapter also corresponds to Chapter 20 in the *Essentials of Consultation-Liaison Psychiatry*.

28.4   An antidepressant that can be used with cancer patients, which has the
        added advantage of simultaneously aiding insomnia and appetite distur-
        bances, and has no anticholinergic side effects, is
        A.   Fluoxetine.
        B.   Trazodone.
        C.   Paroxetine.
        D.   Imipramine.
        E.   Clomipramine.

28.5   Brain metastases are most common in cancer patients with which of the
        following types of cancer?
        A.   Breast cancer.
        B.   Colorectal cancer.
        C.   Melanoma.
        D.   Bladder cancer.
        E.   Kidney cancer.

28.6   Anticancer radiation treatments last an average of
        A.   3–6 weeks.
        B.   6–9 weeks.
        C.   9–12 weeks.
        D.   12–15 weeks.
        E.   6 months.

Directions: For each of the statements below, one or more of the answers is
correct. Choose

        A.   If 1, 2, and 3 are correct.
        B.   If only 1 and 3 are correct.
        C.   If only 2 and 4 are correct.
        D.   If only 4 is correct.
        E.   If all are correct.

28.7   Psychiatric consultation for cancer patients is clearly warranted in cases
        when the patient
        1.   Is highly confrontational in directing anger at the physician.
        2.   Has refused treatment for fatalistic reasons.
        3.   Has persistent depressive symptoms.
        4.   Is in denial about the cancer.

28.8 Ectopic production of hormone by tumors can alter the mental status of cancer patients by
   1. Increasing antidiuretic hormone production and causing low sodium levels.
   2. Increasing parathyroid hormone production and causing low calcium levels.
   3. Increasing adrenocorticotropic hormone production and causing Cushing's syndrome.
   4. Increasing estrogen production and causing dysmenorrhea.

28.9 Maladaptive coping mechanisms on the part of medical staff dealing with cancer patients include
   1. Uncontrolled crying.
   2. Substance abuse.
   3. Absenteeism.
   4. Excessive optimism.

ANSWERS*

28.1 The answer is **B.** Nausea and vomiting in anticipation of chemotherapy can be treated effectively with ondansetron with dexamethasone and lorazepam. **(p. 675)**

28.2 The answer is **D.** A disproportionately high incidence of dysphoria is associated with pancreatic cancer. **(p. 677)**

28.3 The answer is **E.** One of the anticancer medications most commonly associated with affective instability is interferon. **(p. 677)**

28.4 The answer is **B.** An antidepressant that can be used with cancer patients, which has the added advantage of simultaneously aiding insomnia and appetite disturbances, and has no anticholinergic side effects, is trazodone. **(p. 678)**

28.5 The answer is **C.** Brain metastases are most common in cancer patients with melanoma. **(p. 680)**

---

*Page numbers within answer sections refer to *The American Psychiatric Press Textbook of Consultation-Liaison Psychiatry*.

28.6   The answer is **B.** Anticancer radiation treatments last an average of 6–9 weeks. **(p. 681)**

28.7   The answer is **A.** Psychiatric consultation for cancer patients is clearly warranted in cases when the patient is highly confrontational in directing anger at the physician, has refused treatment for fatalistic reasons, or has persistent depressive symptoms. **(p. 673)**

28.8   The answer is **B.** Ectopic production of hormone by tumors can alter the mental status of cancer patients by increasing antidiuretic hormone production and causing low sodium levels and by increasing adrenocorticotropic hormone production and causing Cushing's syndrome. **(p. 681)**

28.9   The answer is **A.** Maladaptive coping mechanisms on the part of medical staff dealing with cancer patients include uncontrolled crying, substance abuse, and absenteeism. **(p. 689)**

Chapter 29

Neurology and Neurosurgery

Directions: Select the single best response for each of the following questions:

29.1 The most common reason for a psychiatric consultation referral from a neurology service is
   A. Suicide attempt.
   B. Diagnosis or evaluation request.
   C. Psychosis.
   D. Eating disorder.
   E. Management of behavior problems.

29.2 Which of the following neuropsychiatric disorders is most prevalent in the general population?
   A. Schizophrenia.
   B. Seizure disorder.
   C. Dementia.
   D. Bipolar disorder.
   E. Multiple sclerosis.

29.3 Which of the following types of lesions are most highly associated with poststroke depression?
   A. Right anterior frontal lesions.
   B. Left anterior frontal lesions.
   C. Right posterior frontal lesions.
   D. Left posterior frontal lesions.
   E. Right dorsal lateral frontal cortical lesions.

This chapter also corresponds to Chapter 21 in the *Essentials of Consultation-Liaison Psychiatry*.

29.4 Central nervous system (CNS) tumors are most commonly found in which of the following regions?
    A. Frontal region.
    B. Temporal region.
    C. Posterior fossa.
    D. Parietal area.
    E. Occipital lobes.

29.5 A brain tumor patient whose symptoms include an akinetic presentation, loss of spontaneous gesturing, decreased speech production, leg weakness, and sensational loss is most likely to have
    A. Frontal convexity syndrome.
    B. An occipital-lobe tumor.
    C. A midline diencephalic tumor.
    D. Medial frontal syndrome.
    E. Orbitofrontal syndrome.

29.6 An epileptic seizure patient who has recurrent attacks of uncontrollable rage most likely has
    A. Interictal behavior syndrome.
    B. Absence seizure disorder.
    C. A temporal-lobe epileptic interictal personality.
    D. Episodic dyscontrol syndrome.
    E. Tonic-clonic seizures.

29.7 Conversion symptoms are most likely to be associated with which of the following degenerative diseases?
    A. Multiple sclerosis.
    B. Amyotrophic lateral sclerosis.
    C. Parkinson's disease.
    D. Friedreich's ataxia.
    E. Huntington's disease.

29.8 A depressed patient with pathological laughing and crying can be treated most effectively with
    A. Trazodone.
    B. Doxepin.
    C. Methylphenidate.
    D. Bupropion.
    E. Amitriptyline.

Directions: For each of the statements below, one or more of the answers is correct. Choose

A. If 1, 2, and 3 are correct.
B. If only 1 and 3 are correct.
C. If only 2 and 4 are correct.
D. If only 4 is correct.
E. If all are correct.

29.9 Faulty comprehension of which of the following deficits suggest a diagnosis of sensory aprosodia in poststroke depression patients?
1. Prosody.
2. Prosodic repetition.
3. Emotional gesturing.
4. Spontaneous prosody.

29.10 Common symptoms of postconcussion syndrome include
1. Dizziness.
2. Headache.
3. Insomnia.
4. Mania.

29.11 Which of the following neurological diseases can be mistaken for a paranoid delusional disorder?
1. Porphyria.
2. Epilepsy.
3. Wernicke's aphasia.
4. Central nervous system neoplastic disease.

29.12 A computed tomography (CT) scan is preferable to a magnetic resonance image (MRI) in evaluating neurology patients if they
1. Are unable to remain immobile.
2. Have a pacemaker.
3. Are uncooperative.
4. Have a head or spine injury that requires rapid evaluation.

ANSWERS*

29.1   The answer is **E.** The most common reason for a psychiatric consultation referral from a neurology service is management of behavior problems. **(p. 697)**

29.2   The answer is **C.** Dementia is most the prevalent of these disorders within the general population. **(p. 698)**

29.3   The answer is **B.** Left anterior frontal lesions are most highly associated with poststroke depression. **(p. 699)**

29.4   The answer is **C.** Central nervous system tumors are most commonly found in the posterior fossa. **(p. 699)**

29.5   The answer is **D.** A brain tumor patient whose symptoms include an akinetic presentation, loss of spontaneous gesturing, decreased speech production, leg weakness, and sensational loss is most likely to have medial frontal syndrome. **(p. 700)**

29.6   The answer is **D.** An epileptic seizure patient who has recurrent attacks of uncontrollable rage is most likely to have episodic dyscontrol syndrome. **(p. 703)**

29.7   The answer is **A.** Conversion symptoms are most likely to be associated with multiple sclerosis. **(pp. 705–706)**

29.8   The answer is **E.** A depressed patient with pathological laughing and crying can be treated most effectively with amitriptyline and nortriptyline. **(p. 712)**

29.9   The answer is **B.** Faulty comprehension of prosody and emotional gesturing suggest a diagnosis of sensory aprosodia in poststroke depression patients. **(p. 699)**

29.10   The answer is **A.** Common symptoms of postconcussion syndrome include dizziness, headache, and insomnia. **(p. 704)**

---

*Page numbers within answer sections refer to *The American Psychiatric Press Textbook of Consultation-Liaison Psychiatry*.

29.11 The answer is **C.** Epilepsy and central nervous system neoplastic disease can be mistaken for a paranoid delusional disorder. **(p. 707)**

29.12 The answer is **E.** A computed tomography scan is preferable to a magnetic resonance image in evaluating neurology patients if they are unable to remain immobile, have a pacemaker, are uncooperative, or have a head or spine injury that requires rapid evaluation. **(p. 710)**

Chapter 30

Obstetrics and Gynecology

Directions: Select the single best response for each of the following questions:

30.1 Gender identity is now believed to be established during
A. The first year of life.
B. The second year of life.
C. The sixth year of life.
D. Adolescence.
E. Latency.

30.2 Which of the following is true?
A. There is no association between clinical depression and menopause.
B. A minority of women in the United States obtain regular gynecological care.
C. Most women for whom hormone replacement therapy is prescribed do not continue the hormones after the first year.
D. All of the above.
E. None of the above.

30.3 The "baby blues" typically resolve within
A. 3 days postpartum.
B. 7 days postpartum.
C. 2 weeks postpartum.
D. 3 weeks postpartum.
E. 1 month postpartum.

This chapter also corresponds to Chapter 22 in the *Essentials of Consultation-Liaison Psychiatry.*

30.4   Which of the following is false?
    A.   A patient with psychotic illness is incompetent to request sterilization.
    B.   Women are typically more comfortable discussing infertility than are men.
    C.   The United States has the highest frequency of adolescent pregnancy in the developed world.
    D.   All of the above.
    E.   None of the above.

30.5   In cases of suspected postpartum child abuse, when the mother's verbal statements or behavior constitutes a threat to the child's safety, which of the following has legal authority to assume protective custody?
    A.   The psychiatric consultant.
    B.   The gynecologist.
    C.   The mother's family.
    D.   The hospital.
    E.   None of the above.

30.6   Consultant psychiatrists working in the obstetrics/gynecology setting should be aware that
    A.   Even well-educated women may find themselves unable to insist that their partners use condoms.
    B.   The incidence of domestic violence decreases during pregnancy.
    C.   Women live longer after a diagnosis of HIV disease than do men.
    D.   All of the above.
    E.   None of the above.

Directions: For each of the statements below, one or more of the answers is correct. Choose

    A.   If 1, 2, and 3 are correct.
    B.   If only 1 and 3 are correct.
    C.   If only 2 and 4 are correct.
    D.   If only 4 is correct.
    E.   If all are correct.

30.7   Psychiatric consultations are likely to be requested for infertility patients with the following conditions:
   1.   Amenorrhea related to eating disorder.
   2.   Unwillingness to terminate fertility treatment despite repeated failure.
   3.   Sexual practices (or lack thereof) responsible for their failure to conceive.
   4.   Unsuccessful attempts to become pregnant for more than 1 year.

30.8   Which of the following are currently considered helpful in treating hyperemesis during pregnancy?
   1.   Stimulus deprivation.
   2.   Supportive psychotherapy.
   3.   Social isolation.
   4.   Relaxation techniques.

30.9   Floppy baby syndrome may result if the following psychotropic medication is used during pregnancy:
   1.   Fluoxetine.
   2.   Haloperidol.
   3.   Chlorpromazine.
   4.   Diazepam.

ANSWERS*

30.1   The answer is **B.** Gender identity is now believed to be established during the second year of life for both boys and girls. **(p. 722)**

30.2   The answer is **D.** All of the statements are true. There is no association between clinical depression and menopause. A minority of women in the United States obtain regular gynecological care. Most women for whom hormone replacement therapy is prescribed do not continue the hormones after the first year. **(pp. 723–724)**

30.3   The answer is **B.** The "baby blues" typically resolve within 7 days postpartum. **(p. 725)**

---

*Page numbers within answer sections refer to *The American Psychiatric Press Textbook of Consultation-Liaison Psychiatry.*

30.4　The answer is **A.** A patient with psychotic illness is not automatically considered incompetent to request sterilization. **(pp. 726–728)**

30.5　The answer is **D.** In cases of suspected postpartum child abuse, when the mother's verbal statements or behavior constitutes a threat to the child's safety, the hospital has legal authority to assume protective custody. **(p. 733)**

30.6　The answer is **A.** Consultant psychiatrists working in the obstetrics/gynecology setting should be aware that even well-educated women may find themselves unable to insist that their partners use condoms. **(p. 735)**
The other statements are false; correct statements are as follows:
Counterintuitively, the incidence of domestic violence increases during pregnancy. **(p. 734)**
In general, women die sooner after a diagnosis of HIV disease than do men. **(p. 734)**

30.7　The answer is **A.** Psychiatric consultations are likely to be requested for infertility patients who also report amenorrhea related to eating disorder, are unwilling to terminate fertility treatment despite repeated failure, and whose sexual practices (or lack thereof) are responsible for their failure to conceive. **(pp. 726–727)**

30.8　The answer is **C.** Supportive psychotherapy and relaxation techniques are currently considered helpful in treating hyperemesis during pregnancy. **(p. 729)**

30.9　The answer is **D.** Floppy baby syndrome may result if diazepam is used during pregnancy. **(p. 731)**

Chapter 31

Pediatrics

QUESTIONS

Directions: Select the single best response for each of the following questions:

31.1   A consultation that would take approximately 1.5 hours with an adult would be expected to take how long if the patient is a child?
A.   2.5 hours.
B.   3.0 hours.
C.   3.5 hours.
D.   4.0 hours.
E.   4.5 hours.

31.2   Professionals whose job is to normalize the hospital environment so that children and their parents can continue functioning and developing despite hospitalization are known as
A.   Parent advocates.
B.   Child life workers.
C.   Pediatric social workers.
D.   Pediatric consultants.
E.   Pediatric nurses.

31.3   An instrument that includes a 10-item checklist for assessment of common coping strategies for children is the
A.   Child Behavior Checklist.
B.   Perceived Competence Scale for Children.
C.   Kidcope.
D.   Child Somatization Inventory.
E.   Child Mental Status Exam.

No corresponding chapter appears in the *Essentials of Consultation-Liaison Psychiatry.*

31.4   Which of the following pharmacological agents would be most likely to be prescribed for a child with attention-deficit/hyperactivity disorder?
A.   Imipramine.
B.   Lorazepam.
C.   Amitriptyline.
D.   Haloperidol.
E.   Methylphenidate.

31.5   Which of the following is true?
A.   The prognosis for malignancies tends to be less favorable among children than among adults.
B.   A substantial number of pediatric patients harm themselves while in the hospital.
C.   Routine observation is more difficult in a pediatric ward compared with an adult ward.
D.   All of the above.
E.   None of the above.

Directions: For each of the statements below, one or more of the answers is correct. Choose

A.   If 1, 2, and 3 are correct.
B.   If only 1 and 3 are correct.
C.   If only 2 and 4 are correct.
D.   If only 4 is correct.
E.   If all are correct.

31.6   Compared with child psychiatrists, pediatricians are
1.   More likely to view childhood as a time of struggle.
2.   Less likely to provide reassurance for patients and their families.
3.   More likely to be familiar with key aspects of the medical system.
4.   Less likely to feel comfortable dealing with anxiety and other strong emotions.

31.7   Analgesics tend to be underutilized in pediatric settings because physicians believe that children
1.   Do not feel pain to the same degree as do adults.
2.   Have a serious risk of addiction.
3.   Are more resilient to pain than adults are.
4.   Will have more serious side effects than adults.

ANSWERS*

31.1   The answer is **E.** A consultation that would take approximately 1.5 hours with an adult would be expected to take 4.5 hours (three times as long) if the patient is a child. **(p. 743)**

31.2   The answer is **B.** Professionals whose job is to normalize the hospital environment so that children and their parents can continue functioning and developing despite hospitalization are known as child life workers. **(p. 744)**

31.3   The answer is **C.** An instrument that includes a 10-item checklist for assessment of common coping strategies for children is the Kidcope. **(p. 745)**

31.4   The answer is **E.** Methylphenidate (a stimulant) is the most likely agent to be prescribed for a child with attention-deficit/hyperactivity disorder. **(pp. 747–748)**

31.5   The answer is **E.** All of the answers are false; correct answers are as follows. The prognosis for malignancies tends to be more favorable among children than among adults. **(p. 749)**
       The number of pediatric patients who harm themselves while in the hospital is small. **(p. 746)**
       Routine observation is easier in a pediatric ward than on an adult ward because patients have less privacy. **(p. 746)**

31.6   The answer is **D.** Compared with child psychiatrists, pediatricians are less likely to feel comfortable dealing with anxiety and other strong emotions. **(p. 742)**

31.7   The answer is **A.** Analgesics tend to be underutilized in pediatric settings because physicians believe that children do not feel pain to the same degree as do adults, have a serious risk of addiction, and are more resilient to pain than adults are. **(p. 748)**

---

*Page numbers within answer sections refer to *The American Psychiatric Press Textbook of Consultation-Liaison Psychiatry.*

Chapter 32

Physical Medicine and Rehabilitation

Directions: Select the single best response for each of the following questions:

32.1   The percentage of disabled Americans who receive some form of rehabilitation is
A.   25%.
B.   40%.
C.   50%.
D.   60%.
E.   75%.

32.2   Which of the following terms is defined by the World Health Organization as "a loss in ability to perform activities of daily living such as walking, talking, dressing, and feeding"?
A.   Handicap.
B.   Rehabilitation.
C.   Impairment.
D.   Disability.
E.   Social phobia.

This chapter also corresponds to Chapter 23 in the *Essentials of Consultation-Liaison Psychiatry.*

32.3   At an inpatient rehabilitation unit that is exempt from diagnostic-related group requirements, patients must be able to tolerate and receive any combination of physical therapy, occupational therapy, and speech therapy for at least
       A.   30 minutes per day.
       B.   3 hours per day.
       C.   5 hours per day.
       D.   3 days per week.
       E.   5 days per week.

32.4   Among those listed, the highest rate of depression is seen in which of the following rehabilitation groups?
       A.   Stroke.
       B.   Spinal cord injury.
       C.   Amputation.
       D.   Cancer.
       E.   Multiple sclerosis.

32.5   Hemineglect is a neurologically based body image problem that is seen most often in patients with which of the following?
       A.   Amputation.
       B.   Nondominant parietal stroke.
       C.   Brain tumor.
       D.   Body dysmorphic disorder.
       E.   Amyotrophic lateral sclerosis.

32.6   The anxiety disorder that most frequently develops poststroke is
       A.   Agoraphobia.
       B.   Posttraumatic stress disorder (PTSD).
       C.   Acute stress disorder.
       D.   Social phobia.
       E.   Generalized anxiety disorder.

32.7   Patients with which of the following problems have proportionately less stage 4 sleep than other persons?
       A.   Hemorrhagic stroke.
       B.   Head and neck cancer.
       C.   Rheumatoid arthritis.
       D.   Spinal cord injury.
       E.   Traumatic brain injury.

32.8   When a rehabilitation patient is being tapered off pain medication, and the pain has been controlled with morphine sulfate, it is recommended that the dosage be tapered off at the rate of
  A.   1% per hour.
  B.   10% per hour.
  C.   1% per day.
  D.   5% per day.
  E.   10% per day.

32.9   Among the following treatments, a rehabilitation patient who is learning how to use a wheelchair and how to overcome access problems is most likely to benefit from
  A.   Biofeedback.
  B.   Operant conditioning.
  C.   Social skills training.
  D.   Psychoeducation.
  E.   Family therapy.

Directions: For each of the statements below, one or more of the answers is correct. Choose

  A.   If 1, 2, and 3 are correct.
  B.   If only 1 and 3 are correct.
  C.   If only 2 and 4 are correct.
  D.   If only 4 is correct.
  E.   If all are correct.

32.10 A psychiatric consultant working in the rehabilitation setting should be able to provide the following service(s):
  1.   Diagnosis.
  2.   Feedback to the staff.
  3.   Medication recommendations.
  4.   An integrated, consistent team plan for patient problems.

32.11 The core rehabilitation team, which is adequate for most patients, usually includes which of the following?
  1.   Physical therapist.
  2.   Psychiatric consultant.
  3.   Occupational therapist.
  4.   Dietary counselor.

32.12   Frequently encountered cognitive problems in rehabilitation medicine include
1.   Vision disturbances.
2.   Apraxia.
3.   Memory disturbances.
4.   Compliance problems.

32.13   Denial in patients undergoing rehabilitation is associated with
1.   Suicidal tendency.
2.   Hemineglect.
3.   Insomnia.
4.   Difficult behavior.

32.14   Sexual dysfunction experienced by patients undergoing rehabilitation for stroke and other disorders is most frequently attributed to
1.   Psychological dysfunction.
2.   Neurological dysfunction.
3.   Vascular dysfunction.
4.   Hormonal dysfunction.

32.15   Which of the following psychopharmacological medications can result in impaired recovery poststroke?
1.   Clonidine.
2.   Lithium.
3.   Carbamazepine.
4.   Haloperidol.

32.16   Psychosocial problems are most likely to arise for outpatient rehabilitation patients when
1.   The patient needs transportation.
2.   The patient and family first recognize the extent of the disability.
3.   The patient ceases going for outpatient follow-up care.
4.   The patient reaches a functional plateau.

ANSWERS*

32.1   The answer is **A.** The percentage of disabled Americans who receive some form of rehabilitation is 25%. **(p. 755)**

32.2   The answer is **D.** Disability is defined by the World Health Organization as "a loss in ability to perform activities of daily living such as walking, talking, dressing, and feeding." **(p. 755)**

32.3   The answer is **B.** At an inpatient rehabilitation unit that is exempt from diagnostic-related group requirements, patients must be able to tolerate and receive any combination of physical therapy, occupational therapy, and speech therapy for at least 3 hours per day. **(p. 756)**

32.4   The answer is **C.** Among those listed, the highest rate of depression is seen in amputation patients. **(p. 759)**

32.5   The answer is **B.** Hemineglect is a neurologically based body image problem that is seen most often in patients with nondominant parietal stroke. **(p. 762)**

32.6   The answer is **A.** The anxiety disorder that most frequently develops poststroke is agoraphobia. **(p. 763)**

32.7   The answer is **D.** Patients with spinal cord injuries have proportionately less stage 4 sleep than other persons. **(p. 765)**

32.8   The answer is **E.** When a rehabilitation patient is being tapered off pain medication, and the pain has been controlled with morphine sulfate, it is recommended that the dosage be tapered off at the rate of 10% per day. **(p. 768)**

32.9   The answer is **C.** A rehabilitation patient who is learning how to use a wheelchair and how to overcome access problems is most likely to benefit from social skills training. **(p. 772)**

---

*Page numbers within answer sections refer to *The American Psychiatric Press Textbook of Consultation-Liaison Psychiatry.*

32.10   The answer is **E.** A psychiatric consultant working in the rehabilitation set-
        ting should be able to provide diagnosis, feedback to the staff, medication
        recommendations, and an integrated, consistent team plan for patient
        problems. **(p. 755)**

32.11   The answer is **B.** The core rehabilitation team, which is adequate for most
        patients, usually includes a physical therapist and an occupational thera-
        pist. **(p. 757)**

32.12   The answer is **A.** Frequently encountered cognitive problems in rehabilita-
        tion medicine include vision disturbances, apraxia, and memory distur-
        bances. **(p. 760)**

32.13   The answer is **C.** Denial in patients undergoing rehabilitation is associated
        with hemineglect or difficult behavior. **(p. 762)**

32.14   The answer is **A.** Sexual dysfunction experienced by patients undergoing
        rehabilitation for stroke and other disorders is most frequently attributed to
        psychological dysfunction, neurological dysfunction, or vascular dysfunc-
        tion. **(p. 766)**

32.15   The answer is **D.** Haloperidol can result in impaired neurological recovery
        poststroke. **(p. 770)**

32.16   The answer is **C.** Psychosocial problems are most likely to arise for outpa-
        tient rehabilitation patients at two points: when the patient and family first
        recognize the extent of the disability and when the patient reaches a func-
        tional plateau. **(p. 774)**

Chapter 33

Intensive Care Units

Directions: Select the single best response for each of the following questions:

33.1 When examining a patient in the intensive care unit (ICU), which of the following should be assessed first?
   A. Level of alertness.
   B. Thought processes.
   C. Recent and remote memory.
   D. Use of vocabulary.
   E. Judgment.

33.2 Formal screening of the cognitive functioning of patients in the intensive care unit (ICU) is usually performed with the
   A. WWHHHIMP.
   B. Mini-Mental State Exam (MMSE).
   C. Millon Clinical Multiaxial Inventory-II (MCMI-II).
   D. Neurobehavioral Cognitive Status Examination (NCSE).
   E. Bender-Gestalt Test.

33.3 When evaluating a patient for psychiatric disturbances in the intensive care unit (ICU), which of the following should the staff ask first?
   A. Is depression present?
   B. Is delirium present?
   C. Is functional psychosis present?
   D. Is mental retardation present?
   E. Does the patient's behavior present an acute danger to self or to others?

This chapter also corresponds to Chapter 24 in the *Essentials of Consultation-Liaison Psychiatry*.

33.4   Life-threatening causes of delirium in the intensive care unit (ICU) include all of the following **EXCEPT**
   A.   Hypertensive encephalopathy.
   B.   Hypoglycemia.
   C.   Hyponatremia.
   D.   Hypoxia.
   E.   Meningitis.

33.5   Which of the following is true?
   A.   The use of psychotropic medications in critically ill patients with psychiatric symptoms is not recommended.
   B.   Delirium that is caused by hypoxia or hypoglycemia can be treated with neuroleptics alone.
   C.   Some critically ill patients require higher doses of psychotropic drugs than do healthy adults.
   D.   All of the above.
   E.   None of the above.

33.6   The medication of choice for acute anxiety in intensive care unit (ICU) patients is
   A.   Haloperidol.
   B.   Clonazepam.
   C.   Alprazolam.
   D.   Lorazepam.
   E.   Diazepam.

33.7   Which of the following is the most likely cause of a confusional state in intensive care unit (ICU) patients?
   A.   Severe anxiety.
   B.   Delirium.
   C.   Anger.
   D.   Pain.
   E.   Psychosis.

33.8   Which of the following are usually considered the medications of first choice for managing delirium in intensive care unit (ICU) patients?
   A.   Neuroleptics.
   B.   Benzodiazepines.
   C.   Narcotics.
   D.   Selective serotonin reuptake inhibitors.
   E.   Paralytic agents.

Directions: For each of the statements below, one or more of the answers is correct. Choose

    A. If 1, 2, and 3 are correct.
    B. If only 1 and 3 are correct.
    C. If only 2 and 4 are correct.
    D. If only 4 is correct.
    E. If all are correct.

33.9   Lower doses of psychotropic medications may be advisable in intensive care unit (ICU) patients with medical illness because of the potential for
    1. Renal impairment.
    2. Adverse drug interactions.
    3. Hepatic impairment.
    4. Greater sensitivity to side effects.

33.10 Side effects that may limit the use of psychostimulants in the treatment of depression in medically ill patients include
    1. Hypotension.
    2. Tachycardia.
    3. Constipation.
    4. Insomnia.

33.11 Drugs associated with delirium when used in the intensive care unit (ICU) include
    1. Cimetidine.
    2. Atropine.
    3. Procainamide.
    4. Clonidine.

33.12 The recommended management for a noncompliant intensive care unit (ICU) patient who is attempting to leave against medical advice includes
    1. Setting strict limits.
    2. Finding a guardian if necessary.
    3. Determining competence.
    4. Administering sedatives.

33.13 The recommended acute management for a self-destructive intensive care unit (ICU) patient who is suicidal includes using
1. Team communication.
2. Physical restraints.
3. Sedatives.
4. Cognitive psychotherapy.

33.14 The recommended management for a patient with a paranoid personality type who is suspicious and frequently quarrelsome with the staff includes
1. Keeping the patient informed about diagnostic and treatment strategies.
2. Using physical restraints.
3. Listening to complaints.
4. Sedating the patient.

33.15 When an intensive care unit (ICU) patient is being weaned from a ventilator, factors that can contribute to the development of delirium include
1. Respiratory insufficiency.
2. Side effects of multiple medications.
3. Metabolic imbalances.
4. Infection.

33.16 The most important factors contributing to delirium following cardiac surgery are
1. History of myocardial infarction.
2. Preexisting brain dysfunction.
3. Panic-level anxiety.
4. Duration and complexity of the surgical procedure.

■ ANSWERS*

33.1 The answer is **A.** When examining a patient in the intensive care unit, the patient's level of alertness should be assessed first. **(p. 784)**

33.2 The answer is **B.** Formal screening of the cognitive functioning of patients in the intensive care unit is usually performed with the Mini-Mental State Exam. **(p. 785)**

---

*Page numbers within answer sections refer to *The American Psychiatric Press Textbook of Consultation-Liaison Psychiatry.*

33.3   The answer is **E.** When evaluating a patient for psychiatric disturbances in the intensive care unit, it is recommended that the staff first ask whether the patient's behavior presents an acute danger to self or to others. If the answer is yes, request a psychiatric consultation. **(p. 786)**

33.4   The answer is **C.** Life-threatening causes of delirium in the intensive care unit include hypertensive encephalopathy, hypoglycemia, hypoxia, and meningitis. **(p. 787)**

33.5   The answer is **C.** Some critically ill patients require higher doses of psychotropic drugs than do healthy adults. **(p. 788)**
The other answers are false; the correct answers are as follows:
When used appropriately, psychotropic medications are generally well tolerated and effective in critically ill patients. **(p. 788)**
Delirium that is caused by hypoxia or hypoglycemia should be treated specifically (e.g., reversal of hypoxia with oxygen or hypoglycemia with glucose). **(p. 785)**

33.6   The answer is **D.** The medication of choice for acute anxiety in intensive care unit patients is lorazepam. **(p. 791)**

33.7   The answer is **B.** Although confused behavior can have severe etiologies, most confusional states experienced by intensive care unit patients are secondary to a medical or substance-induced cause, such as delirium or dementia. **(p. 792)**

33.8   The answer is **A.** Neuroleptics are usually considered the medications of first choice for managing delirium in intensive care unit patients. **(p. 793)**

33.9   The answer is **E.** Lower doses of psychotropic medications may be advisable in intensive care unit patients with medical illness because of the potential for renal impairment, adverse drug interactions, hepatic impairment, and greater sensitivity to side effects in these patients. **(p. 788)**

33.10   The answer is **C.** Side effects that may limit the use of psychostimulants in the treatment of depression in medically ill patients include tachycardia and insomnia. **(p. 792)**

33.11   The answer is **A.** Drugs associated with delirium when used in the intensive care unit include cimetidine, atropine, and procainamide. **(p. 793)**

33.12 The answer is **A.** The recommended management for a noncompliant intensive care unit patient who is attempting to leave against medical advice includes setting strict limits, finding a guardian if necessary, and determining competence. **(p. 796)**

33.13 The answer is **A.** The recommended acute management for a self-destructive intensive care unit patient who is suicidal includes using team communication, physical restraints, and sedatives. **(p. 796)**

33.14 The answer is **B.** The recommended management for a patient with a paranoid personality type who is suspicious and frequently quarrelsome with the staff includes keeping the patient informed about diagnostic and treatment strategies and listening to the patient's complaints. **(p. 797)**

33.15 The answer is **E.** When an intensive care unit patient is being weaned from a ventilator, factors that can contribute to the development of delirium include respiratory insufficiency, the side effects of multiple medications, metabolic imbalances, and infection. **(p. 798)**

33.16 The answer is **C.** The most important factors contributing to delirium following cardiac surgery are preexisting brain dysfunction and duration and complexity of the surgical procedure. **(pp. 798–799)**

Chapter 34

Psychiatric Issues in the Care of Dying Patients

 QUESTIONS

Directions: Select the single best response for each of the following questions:

34.1 Informing dying patients about their need to appoint a proxy
  A. Is recommended if they have also been informed about their poor prognosis.
  B. Is recommended only if they are psychologically healthy.
  C. Is not recommended unless family members agree.
  D. Is required in some states.
  E. Is required under federal law.

34.2 Which of the following is most commonly used in treating acute anxiety experienced by terminally ill patients?
  A. Short-acting benzodiazepines.
  B. Long-acting benzodiazepines.
  C. Neuroleptics.
  D. Tricyclic antidepressants.
  E. Narcotic analgesics.

This chapter also corresponds to Chapter 25 in the *Essentials of Consultation-Liaison Psychiatry*.

34.3   Which of the following is recommended as the most effective model for providing psychological support to dying patients who are experiencing acute anxiety?
A. Cognitive-behavioral therapy.
B. Family therapy.
C. Crisis-oriented psychotherapy.
D. Relaxation and imagery.
E. Psychodynamic psychotherapy.

34.4   In diagnosing major depression in a terminally ill cancer patient, a clinician who attempts to determine whether the physical symptom of fatigue is a result of a depressive disorder or of the cancer itself is employing which of the following approaches?
A. Inclusive approach.
B. Etiological approach.
C. Exclusive approach.
D. Substitutive approach.
E. None of the above.

34.5   The Endicott substitution criteria used for the measurement of depression when a patient has the physical symptom of a change in appetite is
A. Brooding, self-pity.
B. Tearfulness, depressed appearance.
C. Social withdrawal.
D. Lack of reactivity.
E. Indecisiveness.

34.6   "The intentional termination of a patient's life by a physician" is most accurately defined by the term
A. Active euthanasia.
B. Passive euthanasia.
C. Voluntary euthanasia.
D. Physician-assisted suicide.
E. Rational suicide.

34.7   In contrast to delirium in terminally ill patients, dementia in terminally ill patients is characterized by all of the following **EXCEPT**
    A.   Chronic, progressive onset.
    B.   Short-term memory impairment.
    C.   Long-term memory impairment.
    D.   Irreversibility.
    E.   Severe impairment of the sleep-wake cycle.

34.8   The medication of choice for treatment of delirium in the dying patient is
    A.   Lorazepam.
    B.   Midazolam.
    C.   Haloperidol.
    D.   Chlorpromazine.
    E.   Methotrimeprazine.

Directions: For each of the statements below, one or more of the answers is correct. Choose

    A.   If 1, 2, and 3 are correct.
    B.   If only 1 and 3 are correct.
    C.   If only 2 and 4 are correct.
    D.   If only 4 is correct.
    E.   If all are correct.

34.9   A dying patient with depression who has less than 3 weeks to live should be treated with
    1.   A selective serotonin reuptake inhibitor.
    2.   A tricyclic antidepressant.
    3.   A sedative.
    4.   A rapid-acting psychostimulant.

34.10   A dying patient with depression who is within hours to days of death should be treated with
    1.   Narcotic infusions.
    2.   A selective serotonin reuptake inhibitor.
    3.   A benzodiazepine.
    4.   A rapid-acting psychostimulant.

34.11   A dying patient with agitation and depression accompanied by insomnia is
        best treated with
        1.   A selective serotonin reuptake inhibitor.
        2.   Doxepin.
        3.   A rapid-acting psychostimulant.
        4.   Amitriptyline.

34.12   The use of electroconvulsive therapy (ECT) can be considered for a dying
        patient under the following conditions:
        1.   The patient has mixed depression and anxiety symptoms.
        2.   The patient has a psychotic depression.
        3.   Supportive psychotherapy has not been effective.
        4.   Antidepressant therapy poses unacceptable side effects.

34.13   Pain medications with short half-lives include
        1.   Morphine.
        2.   Methadone.
        3.   Hydromorphine.
        4.   Levorphanol.

34.14   Which of the following analgesic medications is available in a transdermal
        patch?
        1.   Morphine.
        2.   Oxycodone.
        3.   Meperidine.
        4.   Fentanyl.

ANSWERS*

34.1   The answer is **E.** Informing dying patients about their need to appoint a
        proxy is required under federal law. **(p. 808)**

34.2   The answer is **A.** Short-acting benzodiazepines are the medications most
        commonly used in treating acute anxiety experienced by terminally ill pa-
        tients. **(p. 810)**

---

*Page numbers within answer sections refer to *The American Psychiatric Press Textbook
of Consultation-Liaison Psychiatry*.

34.3   The answer is **C**. Crisis-oriented psychotherapy is recommended as the most effective model for providing psychological support to dying patients who are experiencing acute anxiety. **(p. 811)**

34.4   The answer is **B**. In diagnosing major depression in a terminally ill cancer patient, a clinician who attempts to determine whether the physical symptom of fatigue is a result of a depressive disorder or of the cancer itself is employing an etiological approach. **(p. 812)**

34.5   The answer is **B**. The Endicott substitution criteria used for the measurement of depression when a patient has the physical symptom of a change in appetite is tearfulness and a depressed appearance. **(p. 812)**

34.6   The answer is **A**. "The intentional termination of a patient's life by a physician" is most accurately defined by the term *active euthanasia.* **(p. 818)**

34.7   The answer is **E**. In contrast to delirium in terminally ill patients, dementia in terminally ill patients is characterized by chronic, progressive onset; short-term memory impairment; long-term memory impairment; and irreversibility. **(p. 821)**

34.8   The answer is **C**. The medication of choice for treatment of delirium in the dying patient is haloperidol. **(p. 822)**

34.9   The answer is **D**. A dying patient with depression who has less than 3 weeks to live should be treated with a rapid-acting psychostimulant. **(p. 813)**

34.10   The answer is **B**. A dying patient with depression who is within hours to days of death should be treated with narcotic infusions or a benzodiazepine. **(p. 813)**

34.11   The answer is **C**. A dying patient with agitation and depression accompanied by insomnia is best treated with doxepin or amitriptyline. **(p. 814)**

34.12   The answer is **C**. The use of electroconvulsive therapy can be considered for a dying patient when the patient has a psychotic depression or when antidepressant therapy poses unacceptable side effects. **(p. 816)**

34.13   The answer is **B.** Pain medications with short half-lives include morphine and hydromorphine. **(p. 825)**

34.14   The answer is **D.** Fentanyl is available in a transdermal patch. **(p. 826)**

Chapter 35

HIV Disease/AIDS

Directions: Select the single best response for each of the following questions:

35.1 The differential diagnosis of HIV-related mental status changes includes all of the following **EXCEPT**
   A. Metabolic abnormalities.
   B. Medication side effects.
   C. DSM-IV Axis II disorders.
   D. Hypoxic encephalopathy.
   E. Neoplasms.

35.2 According to the DSM-IV classification, the neurodegenerative disorder associated with HIV infection is called
   A. HIV dementia.
   B. HIV-1-associated cognitive/motor complex.
   C. AIDS dementia complex.
   D. HIV-1 encephalopathy.
   E. Dementia due to HIV disease.

35.3 A patient with AIDS dementia complex who cannot walk but is able to perform the basic activities of daily living is at which of the following stages according to the Memorial Sloan-Kettering Clinical Staging System?
   A. Stage 0.5.
   B. Stage 1.
   C. Stage 2.

This chapter also corresponds to Chapter 26 in the *Essentials of Consultation-Liaison Psychiatry*.

D. Stage 3.

E. Stage 4.

35.4   The neuropsychiatric complication that occurs most frequently in hospitalized AIDS patients is

A. Psychosis.

B. Mania.

C. Seizure disorder.

D. Delirium.

E. HIV-1 central nervous system infection.

35.5   The drug(s) of choice for HIV-related psychosis are

A. Anticonvulsants.

B. Lithium.

C. Paralytic agents.

D. Neuroleptics.

E. Benzodiazepines.

35.6   Which of the following is true?

A. Hospitalized HIV/AIDS patients with Axis II disorders should be managed with the psychologically least regressing approach.

B. Men may experience greater AIDS-related bereavement than do women.

C. Nonwhite HIV/AIDS patients are more likely to attempt suicide than whites.

D. All of the above.

E. None of the above.

35.7   Which of the following is false?

A. Active injection drug use appears to enhance the progression of HIV disease.

B. Among gay and bisexual men with HIV disease, the majority are alcohol dependent.

C. Psychotherapy is the therapeutic mainstay for treatment of adjustment disorders in patients with HIV disease.

D. All of the above.

E. None of the above.

35.8   The most common pain syndrome in patients with HIV disease is

A. Peripheral neuropathy.

B. Headache.

    C.   Joint pain.

    D.   Postherpetic neuralgia.

    E.   Psychogenic.

35.9   If therapy with analgesics worsens delirium in the terminal states of HIV disease, which of the following is recommended to reduce delirium and allow for adequate pain relief?

    A.   A high-dose opiate.

    B.   A low-dose anticonvulsant.

    C.   An antiarrhythmic.

    D.   Combination antiretroviral therapy.

    E.   Low-dose haloperidol.

Directions: For each of the statements below, one or more of the answers is correct. Choose

    A.   If 1, 2, and 3 are correct.

    B.   If only 1 and 3 are correct.

    C.   If only 2 and 4 are correct.

    D.   If only 4 is correct.

    E.   If all are correct.

35.10 Current trends with respect to inpatient psychiatric consultations for patients with HIV disease include

    1.   More of the HIV/AIDS patients seen as inpatients by consultants are acutely ill at the time of consultation.

    2.   Psychiatric consultations with HIV/AIDS inpatients are becoming more frequent.

    3.   More HIV/AIDS patients are dying at home rather than in hospitals.

    4.   The average length of hospital stays for HIV/AIDS patients is increasing.

35.11 The potential neuropsychiatric side effects of zidovudine include

    1.   Depression.

    2.   Mania.

    3.   Irritability.

    4.   Hallucinations.

35.12 HIV-1 is highly neurotropic and infects

    1.   The brain parenchyma.

    2.   Endothelial cells.

   3. The spinal cord.
   4. Neurons.

35.13 In vitro high concentrations of gp120 can directly cause neuronal death
       through activation of
       1. Sodium channels.
       2. Calcium channels.
       3. Macrophages.
       4. *N*-methyl-D-aspartate (NMDA)-glutamate receptors.

35.14 The American Academy of Neurology's diagnostic criteria for
       HIV-1-associated cognitive/motor complex include a decline in motiva-
       tion or emotional control or change in social behavior characterized by
       1. Apathy.
       2. Aphasia.
       3. Irritability.
       4. Memory loss.

35.15 Cerebrospinal fluid examination of patients with AIDS dementia complex
       may show
       1. Pleocytosis.
       2. Elevated levels of immunoglobulin G.
       3. Oligoclonal bands.
       4. Increased levels of protein.

35.16 Which of the following tests are sensitive to HIV-related cognitive deficits?
       1. Finger Tapping Test.
       2. Grooved Pegboard Test.
       3. Stroop Color/Word Interference Test.
       4. Mini-Mental State Exam (MMSE).

35.17 Factors associated with major depression in HIV-1-infected patients
       include
       1. Unemployment.
       2. Unresolved grief.
       3. Lower level of education.
       4. History of mood disorders.

35.18 In selecting pharmacotherapy for patients with HIV-related major depres-
       sion, the consulting physician should avoid agents that
       1. Block dopamine receptors.
       2. Are potent α-adrenergic antagonists.

3. Have sustained-release delivery.
4. Have anticholinergic effects.

ANSWERS*

35.1 The answer is **C.** The differential diagnosis of HIV-related mental status changes includes metabolic abnormalities, medication side effects, hypoxic encephalopathy, and neoplasms. **(p. 840)**

35.2 The answer is **E.** According to the DSM-IV classification, the neuro-degenerative disorder associated with HIV infection is called dementia due to HIV disease. **(p. 842)**

35.3 The answer is **C.** A patient with AIDS dementia complex who cannot walk but is able to perform the basic activities of daily living is at Stage 2 according to the Memorial Sloan-Kettering Clinical Staging System. **(p. 843)**

35.4 The answer is **D.** The neuropsychiatric complication that occurs most frequently in hospitalized AIDS patients is delirium. **(p. 848)**

35.5 The answer is **D.** The drug(s) of choice for HIV-related psychosis are neuroleptics. **(p. 850)**

35.6 The answer is **A.** Hospitalized HIV/AIDS patients with Axis II disorders should be managed with the psychologically least regressing approach. **(p. 858)**
The other answers are false; correct answers are as follows:
Women may experience greater AIDS-related bereavement than do men. **(p. 857)**
White HIV/AIDS patients are more likely to attempt suicide than non-whites. **(p. 860)**

35.7 The answer is **B.** Among gay and bisexual men with HIV disease, only 2%–9% are alcohol dependent. **(p. 864)**

35.8 The answer is **A.** The most common pain syndrome in patients with HIV disease is peripheral neuropathy. **(p. 866)**

---

*Page numbers within answer sections refer to *The American Psychiatric Press Textbook of Consultation-Liaison Psychiatry.*

35.9   The answer is **E**. If therapy with analgesics worsens delirium in the termi-
        nal states of HIV disease, low-dose haloperidol is recommended to reduce
        delirium and allow for adequate pain relief. **(p. 867)**

35.10   The answer is **B**. More of the HIV/AIDS patients seen as inpatients by con-
        sultants are acutely ill at the time of consultation; more HIV/AIDS patients
        are dying at home rather than in hospitals. **(p. 838)**

35.11   The answer is **A**. The potential neuropsychiatric side effects of zidovudine
        include depression, mania, and irritability. **(p. 839)**

35.12   The answer is **A**. HIV-1 is highly neurotropic and infects the brain paren-
        chyma, endothelial cells, and the spinal cord. **(p. 840)**

35.13   The answer is **C**. In vitro high concentrations of gp120 can directly cause
        neuronal death through activation of calcium channels and *N*-methyl-D-
        aspartate (NMDA)-glutamate receptors. **(p. 841)**

35.14   The answer is **B**. The American Academy of Neurology's diagnostic criteria
        for HIV-1-associated cognitive/motor complex include a decline in moti-
        vation or emotional control or change in social behavior characterized by
        apathy or irritability. **(p. 844)**

35.15   The answer is **E**. Cerebrospinal fluid examination of patients with AIDS de-
        mentia complex may show pleocytosis, elevated levels of immunoglobu-
        lin G, oligoclonal bands, and increased levels of protein. **(p. 845)**

35.16   The answer is **A**. The Finger Tapping Test, Grooved Pegboard Test, and
        Stroop Color/Word Interference Test are sensitive to HIV-related cognitive
        deficits. **(p. 846)**

35.17   The answer is **E**. Factors associated with major depression in HIV-1-
        infected patients include unemployment, unresolved grief, lower level of
        education, and history of mood disorders. **(p. 853)**

35.18   The answer is **C**. In selecting pharmacotherapy for patients with HIV-
        related major depression, the consulting physician should avoid agents
        that are potent α-adrenergic antagonists or have anticholinergic effects.
        (p. 854)

Chapter 36

Geriatric Medicine

Directions: Select the single best response for each of the following questions:

36.1 According to the model proposed by Small and Fawzy, the elderly patient is the central focus of which of the following services?
A. General medicine.
B. Geriatric medicine.
C. Geriatric psychiatry.
D. Consultation-liaison psychiatry.
E. All of the above.

36.2 The highest suicide rate for any age group in the United States is among
A. 15- to 20-year-old men.
B. 55- to 65-year-old men.
C. 55- to 65-year-old women.
D. Men 65 and older.
E. Women 65 and older.

36.3 According to DSM-IV, the age at onset for schizophrenia is defined as
A. Before age 45.
B. Before age 55.
C. Before age 65.
D. Before age 70.
E. No age at onset criterion.

36.4 Compared with a man in his 30s, after a standard alcohol load, an average 60-year-old man will have a blood alcohol level that is
A. 10% higher.
B. 10% lower.

This chapter also corresponds to Chapter 27 in the *Essentials of Consultation-Liaison Psychiatry.*

    C. 20% higher.
    D. 20% lower.
    E. Equal.

36.5   Decreased protein intake and decreased muscle mass in older patients can
        lead to
        A. Overestimation of renal function.
        B. Underestimation of renal function.
        C. Overestimation of liver function.
        D. Underestimation of liver function.
        E. None of the above.

36.6   Which of the following medications provides an advantage for geriatric
        use as a result of its lack of anticholinergic and cardiac side effects?
        A. Doxepin.
        B. Sertraline.
        C. Amitriptyline.
        D. Imipramine.
        E. None of the above.

36.7   The treatment of choice for elderly patients with psychotic depression is
        A. Individual psychodynamic psychotherapy.
        B. Neuroleptics.
        C. Benzodiazepines.
        D. Lithium.
        E. Electroconvulsive therapy (ECT).

36.8   If an elderly patient has symptoms of depression and also has
        psychomotor retardation, which of the following is recommended as
        first-line therapy?
        A. Fluoxetine.
        B. Tranylcypromine.
        C. Trazodone.
        D. Lithium.
        E. Electroconvulsive therapy (ECT).

Directions: For each of the statements below, one or more of the answers is
correct. Choose

    A. If 1, 2, and 3 are correct.
    B. If only 1 and 3 are correct.

    C. If only 2 and 4 are correct.
    D. If only 4 is correct.
    E. If all are correct.

36.9 The early clinical features of delirium in elderly patients include
    1. Irritability.
    2. Sleep disturbances.
    3. Agitation.
    4. Diminished vision.

36.10 Compared with young adult depressed patients, geriatric patients who are clinically depressed are more likely to
    1. Express guilt.
    2. Deny their depressed mood.
    3. Accept a psychological explanation for their illness.
    4. Become preoccupied with somatic symptoms.

36.11 Warning signs that a caregiver may be engaging in elder abuse include
    1. Expressions of frustration about caregiving.
    2. Signs of psychological distress.
    3. History of abuse or violence.
    4. History of alcohol or drug abuse.

36.12 For which of the following drugs would elderly persons have greater receptor-site sensitivity?
    1. Propranolol.
    2. Lithium.
    3. Doxepin.
    4. Diazepam.

ANSWERS*

36.1 The answer is **E.** According to the model proposed by Small and Fawzy, the elderly patient is the central focus of general medicine, geriatric medicine, geriatric psychiatry, and consultation-liaison psychiatry. **(p. 882)**

---

*Page numbers within answer sections refer to *The American Psychiatric Press Textbook of Consultation-Liaison Psychiatry.*

36.2   The answer is **D**. The highest suicide rate for any age group in the United States is among men 65 and older. **(p. 885)**

36.3   The answer is **E**. According to DSM-IV, there is no age at onset criterion for schizophrenia. **(p. 885)**

36.4   The answer is **C**. Compared with a man in his 30s, after a standard alcohol load, an average 60-year-old man will have a blood alcohol level that is 20% higher. **(p. 886)**

36.5   The answer is **A**. Decreased protein intake and decreased muscle mass in older patients can lead to an overestimation of renal function. **(p. 888)**

36.6   The answer is **B**. Sertraline provides an advantage for geriatric use as a result of its lack of anticholinergic and cardiac side effects. **(p. 890)**

36.7   The answer is **E**. The treatment of choice for elderly patients with psychotic depression is electroconvulsive therapy. **(p. 893)**

36.8   The answer is **A**. If an elderly patient has symptoms of depression and also has psychomotor retardation, a nonsedating agent such as fluoxetine is recommended as first-line therapy. **(p. 895)**

36.9   The answer is **A**. The early clinical features of delirium in elderly patients include irritability, sleep disturbances, and agitation. **(p. 883)**

36.10   The answer is **C**. Compared with young adult depressed patients, geriatric patients who are clinically depressed are more likely to deny their depressed mood and become preoccupied with somatic symptoms. **(p. 883)**

36.11   The answer is **E**. Warning signs that a caregiver may be engaging in elder abuse include expressions of frustration about caregiving, signs of psychological distress, a history of abuse or violence, and a history of alcohol or drug abuse. **(p. 886)**

36.12   The answer is **D**. Elderly persons have greater receptor-site sensitivity for diazepam. **(p. 889)**

Chapter 37

Medical-Psychiatric Units

QUESTIONS

Directions: Select the single best response for each of the following questions:

37.1   Which of the following patient groups tends to be underrepresented in medical-psychiatric units?
   A.   Medically ill elderly patients.
   B.   Patients with Parkinson's disease.
   C.   Patients with psychiatric sequelae of stroke.
   D.   Patients with somatoform disorders.
   E.   Patients with chronic pain.

37.2   A Type III medical-psychiatric unit has
   A.   Low to high psychiatric acuity and low medical acuity.
   B.   Low psychiatric acuity and medium to high medical acuity.
   C.   High psychiatric acuity and low medical acuity.
   D.   High psychiatric acuity and medium medical acuity.
   E.   High psychiatric acuity and high medical acuity.

37.3   An increase in which of the following at a medical-psychiatric unit can lead a hospital to apply for TEFRA cap relief?
   A.   Geriatric admissions.
   B.   Nursing staff attrition.
   C.   Complexity of the cases treated.
   D.   Medicare reimbursement.
   E.   Length of stay.

No corresponding chapter appears in the *Essentials of Consultation-Liaison Psychiatry*.

37.4   The critical variable in controlling costs on both diagnosis-related group
        and diagnosis-related group–exempt units is
        A. Utilization of ancillary services.
        B. Length of stay.
        C. Development of outpatient service options.
        D. Number of Medicare discharges.
        E. Case-mix of public versus private patients.

37.5   Which of the following is true?
        A. The medical director of a medical-psychiatric unit establishes its mis-
            sion and goals.
        B. Electroconvulsive therapy (ECT) is an essential treatment capability
            for most Type III units.
        C. Most medical-psychiatric units are operated on a medical model of
            staffing and organization.
        D. All of the above.
        E. None of the above.

Directions: For each of the statements below, one or more of the answers is
correct. Choose

        A. If 1, 2, and 3 are correct.
        B. If only 1 and 3 are correct.
        C. If only 2 and 4 are correct.
        D. If only 4 is correct.
        E. If all are correct.

37.6   Which of the following procedures are typically available on a medical-
        psychiatric unit for a patient with low psychiatric acuity?
        1. Behavior modification.
        2. Electroconvulsive therapy (ECT).
        3. Amytal interviews.
        4. Quiet room observation.

37.7   A Type III medical-psychiatric unit has the ability to manage patients with
        1. Angina.
        2. AIDS.
        3. Chronic obstructive pulmonary disease.
        4. Stroke.

37.8   Admission to a Type III medical-psychiatric unit is automatic for patients
       with
       1. Suicidal depression as well as a medical condition.
       2. Delirium.
       3. Medically unstable drug overdose.
       4. The need to immediately determine whether the problem is medical
           or psychiatric.

37.9   Therapeutic modalities offered for specific patient populations by medi-
       cal-psychiatric units include
       1. Occupational activity groups.
       2. Group education programs.
       3. Recreational activity groups.
       4. Discussion groups.

37.10 Group psychotherapy is appropriate for those geriatric patients who
       1. Have impaired impulse control.
       2. Are intolerant of personal closeness.
       3. Are mute.
       4. Are adapting to illness.

ANSWERS*

37.1   The answer is **D.** Patients with somatoform disorders tend to be
       underrepresented in medical-psychiatric units. **(p. 902)**

37.2   The answer is **D.** A Type III medical-psychiatric unit has high psychiatric
       acuity and medium medical acuity. **(p. 905)**

37.3   The answer is **C.** An increase in the complexity of the cases treated at a
       medical-psychiatric unit can lead a hospital to apply for TEFRA cap relief.
       (p. 912)

37.4   The answer is **B.** The critical variable in controlling costs on both diagno-
       sis-related group and diagnosis-related group–exempt units is length of
       stay. **(p. 912)**

---

*Page numbers within answer sections refer to *The American Psychiatric Press Textbook
of Consultation-Liaison Psychiatry.*

37.5   The answer is **D.** All of the answers are true. The medical director of a med-
        ical-psychiatric unit establishes its mission and goals. Electroconvulsive
        therapy is an essential treatment capability for most Type III units. Most
        medical-psychiatric units are operated on a medical model of staffing and
        organization. **(pp. 905–907)**

37.6   The answer is **A.** Procedures typically available on a medical-psychiatric
        unit for a patient with low psychiatric acuity include behavior modifica-
        tion, electroconvulsive therapy, and Amytal interviews. **(p. 904)**

37.7   The answer is **B.** A Type III medical-psychiatric unit has the ability to
        manage patients with angina and chronic obstructive pulmonary disease.
        (p. 905)

37.8   The answer is **A.** Admission to a Type III medical-psychiatric unit is auto-
        matic for patients with suicidal depression as well as a medical condition,
        delirium, and a medically unstable drug overdose. **(p. 907)**

37.9   The answer is **E.** Therapeutic modalities offered for specific patient popu-
        lations by medical-psychiatric units include occupational activity groups,
        group education programs, recreational activity groups, and discussion
        groups. **(p. 908)**

37.10   The answer is **D.** Group psychotherapy is appropriate for those geriatric
        patients who are adapting to illness. **(p. 908)**

Chapter 38

The Emergency Department

Directions: Select the single best response for each of the following questions:

38.1 If a patient produces a weapon in the presence of a consulting psychiatrist in the emergency department, the clinician should
A. Immediately summon additional staff members.
B. Immediately call the police.
C. Instruct the patient to hand the weapon to him or her directly.
D. Instruct the patient to place the weapon on a flat surface.
E. Allow the patient to hold the weapon in plain view.

38.2 Among the following requests, which is made most frequently by patients entering an emergency psychiatric walk-in clinic?
A. Clarification.
B. Medical advice.
C. Reality contact.
D. Confession.
E. Administrative action.

38.3 For rapid control of acute psychosis in the emergency department setting, which of the following treatments is preferred?
A. Intravenous haloperidol.
B. Intramuscular haloperidol.
C. Intramuscular thioridazine.
D. Combination intramuscular haloperidol and lorazepam.
E. Combination intramuscular haloperidol and benztropine mesylate.

This chapter also corresponds to Chapter 28 in the *Essentials of Consultation-Liaison Psychiatry*.

38.4   Most of the violent behavior that is manifested in the emergency department
        A.   Takes place in the early morning hours.
        B.   Is a result of organic brain syndrome.
        C.   Occurs in the context of family strife.
        D.   Involves a firearm.
        E.   Results in physical injury to the consultant.

38.5   When delirium tremens begins in the emergency department, the recommended initial treatment is
        A.   Lorazepam.
        B.   Diazepam.
        C.   Midazolam.
        D.   Chlordiazepoxide.
        E.   Haloperidol.

38.6   The single most significant criterion for the decision to hospitalize a patient from the emergency department is
        A.   Managed care constraints.
        B.   Dangerousness.
        C.   Homelessness.
        D.   Severity of symptoms.
        E.   The absence of a social support network.

Directions: For each of the statements below, one or more of the answers is correct. Choose

        A.   If 1, 2, and 3 are correct.
        B.   If only 1 and 3 are correct.
        C.   If only 2 and 4 are correct.
        D.   If only 4 is correct.
        E.   If all are correct.

38.7   Among patients seen in the emergency department for psychiatric evaluation or treatment, which of the following characteristics distinguishes patients who carry weapons from those who do not?
        1.   Suicidality.
        2.   Male gender.
        3.   Antisocial personality disorder.
        4.   History of substance abuse.

38.8   When a threatening or agitated patient is first brought into the emergency
        department, which of the following measures should the clinician initially
        consider using?
        1. Physically restrain the patient.
        2. Offer medication to the patient.
        3. Seclude the patient.
        4. Speak calmly to the patient.

38.9   Before a psychiatric patient is transferred from the emergency department
        to another hospital, which of the following should be considered?
        1. Is the proposed receiving facility the correct one?
        2. Is the patient medically stable?
        3. Is the patient showing transient or reversible symptoms?
        4. Is the patient's family in agreement?

38.10   Which components of the neuropsychiatric examination warrant special
        emphasis in emergency psychiatric patients?
        1. Physical appearance.
        2. Memory.
        3. Speech and language.
        4. Abstracting ability.

38.11   When evaluating a patient with an acute change in mental status or behav-
        ior in the emergency department, the consultant should include a urine
        sample to detect
        1. Cocaine.
        2. Alcohol.
        3. Opiates.
        4. Antidepressants.

38.12   Risk factors for suicide among emergency psychiatric patients include
        1. Unemployment.
        2. Major depression.
        3. Never being married.
        4. Terminal illness.

38.13   Nearly half of patients who come to primary care and emergency facilities with somatic complaints for which no organic basis is identified are commonly given the diagnosis of
1. A psychotic disorder.
2. Panic disorder.
3. Borderline personality disorder.
4. Depression.

38.14   Antisocial personality disorder is characterized by
1. Impulsivity.
2. Poor behavior controls.
3. Irresponsibility.
4. Lack of self-assurance.

ANSWERS*

38.1   The answer is **D.** If a patient produces a weapon in the presence of a consulting psychiatrist in the emergency department, the clinician should instruct the patient to place the weapon on a flat surface. **(p. 917)**

38.2   The answer is **A.** One of the most frequent requests made by patients entering an emergency psychiatric walk-in clinic is for clarification. **(p. 919)**

38.3   The answer is **D.** For rapid control of acute psychosis in the emergency department setting, the preferred treatment is a combination of intramuscular haloperidol and lorazepam. **(p. 923)**

38.4   The answer is **C.** Most of the violent behavior that is manifested in the emergency department occurs in the context of family strife. **(p. 927)**

38.5   The answer is **B.** When delirium tremens begins in the emergency department, the recommended initial treatment is diazepam. **(p. 929)**

38.6   The answer is **B.** The single most significant criterion for the decision to hospitalize a patient from the emergency department is dangerousness. **(p. 940)**

---

*Page numbers within answer sections refer to *The American Psychiatric Press Textbook of Consultation-Liaison Psychiatry*.

38.7   The answer is **C**. Among patients seen in the emergency department for psychiatric evaluation or treatment, male gender and a history of substance abuse distinguish patients who carry weapons from those who do not. **(p. 916)**

38.8   The answer is **C**. When a threatening or agitated patient is first brought into the emergency department, the clinician should initially offer medication to the patient and speak calmly to him or her. **(p. 917)**

38.9   The answer is **A**. Before a psychiatric patient is transferred from the emergency department to another hospital, the consultant should consider whether the proposed receiving facility is the correct one, whether the patient is medically stable, and whether the patient is showing transient or reversible symptoms. **(p. 918)**

38.10   The answer is **B**. Components of the neuropsychiatric examination that warrant special emphasis in emergency psychiatric patients include physical appearance and speech and language. **(p. 920)**

38.11   The answer is **B**. When evaluating a patient with an acute change in mental status or behavior in the emergency department, the consultant should include a urine sample to detect cocaine and opiates. **(p. 921)**

38.12   The answer is **E**. Risk factors for suicide among emergency psychiatric patients include unemployment, major depression, never being married, and terminal illness. **(p. 926)**

38.13   The answer is **C**. Nearly half of patients who come to primary care and emergency facilities with somatic complaints for which no organic basis is identified are commonly given the diagnosis of panic disorder or depression. **(p. 936)**

38.14   The answer is **A**. Antisocial personality disorder is characterized by impulsivity, poor behavior controls, and irresponsibility. **(p. 937)**

Chapter 39

The Consultation-Liaison Psychiatrist in the Primary Care Clinic

Directions: Select the single best response for each of the following questions:

39.1   The percentage of primary care patients with well-defined anxiety or depressive disorder is
   A.   10%–15%.
   B.   16%–20%.
   C.   21%–25%.
   D.   26%–30%.
   E.   31%–35%.

39.2   How many new psychiatric consultation requests would a typical primary care clinic of 10 physicians be expected to generate per week?
   A.   2–3.
   B.   5–6.
   C.   8–9.
   D.   11–12.
   E.   14–15.

This chapter also corresponds to Chapter 29 in the *Essentials of Consultation-Liaison Psychiatry*.

39.3   Primary care–based treatment of depression usually emphasizes
        A.   Brief individual psychotherapy.
        B.   Long-term individual psychotherapy.
        C.   Group psychotherapy.
        D.   Electroconvulsive therapy (ECT).
        E.   Antidepressant medication.

39.4   Which of the following is true?
        A.   The primary care clinic is an optimal setting for ongoing psychotherapy.
        B.   Half of physician visits from patients with explicit psychiatric diagnoses occur in primary care clinics.
        C.   Patient confidentiality must always be preserved in the primary care clinic.
        D.   All of the above.
        E.   None of the above.

Directions: For each of the statements below, one or more of the answers is correct. Choose

        A.   If 1, 2, and 3 are correct.
        B.   If only 1 and 3 are correct.
        C.   If only 2 and 4 are correct.
        D.   If only 4 is correct.
        E.   If all are correct.

39.5   A consultant's satisfaction with outpatient consultation work will be enhanced by
        1.   Flexibility.
        2.   Willingness to work with a wide range of patients.
        3.   An eclectic approach.
        4.   Choosing those referrals that best fit his or her clinical style.

39.6   Outpatient psychiatric consultation for the patient who somatizes should focus on
        1.   Reducing symptoms.
        2.   Prescribing psychotropic medication.
        3.   Restoring function.
        4.   Finding the medical cause of symptoms.

ANSWERS*

39.1 The answer is **A.** The percentage of primary care patients with well-defined anxiety or depressive disorder is 10%–15%. **(p. 948)**

39.2 The answer is **A.** A typical primary care clinic of 10 physicians would be expected to generate 2–3 new consultation requests per week. **(p. 951)**

39.3 The answer is **E.** Primary care–based treatment of depression usually emphasizes antidepressant medication. **(p. 953)**

39.4 The answer is **B.** Half of physician visits from patients with explicit psychiatric diagnoses occur in primary care clinics. **(p. 948)**
The other answers are false; correct answers are as follows:
The primary care clinic is rarely the best setting for ongoing psychotherapy. **(p. 950)**
Patient confidentiality cannot always be preserved in the primary care clinic. **(p. 950)**

39.5 The answer is **A.** A consultant's satisfaction with outpatient consultation work will be enhanced by flexibility, a willingness to work with a wide range of patients, and an eclectic approach. **(p. 951)**

39.6 The answer is **A.** Outpatient psychiatric consultation for the patient who somatizes should focus on reducing symptoms and restoring function. If the patient has a well-defined anxiety or depressive disorder, specific treatment (such as psychotropics) are likely to relieve symptoms. **(p. 952)**

---

*Page numbers within answer sections refer to *The American Psychiatric Press Textbook of Consultation-Liaison Psychiatry.*

Section IV

Treatment

Chapter 40

Psychopharmacology

Directions: Select the single best response for each of the following questions:

40.1   To avoid a frightening dystonic reaction after the introduction of an antipsychotic medication for an anxious patient who is experiencing an initial episode of schizophrenia, prophylactic treatment with which of the following medications is recommended?
A. Lithium.
B. Bupropion.
C. Benztropine.
D. Doxepin.
E. Clozapine.

40.2   The term *bimodal relatedness* refers to
A. Combination therapy with drugs from two different classes.
B. Interacting with a patient taking into account both the physico-chemical system and the psychosocial dimension.
C. Interacting with a patient taking into account both the social and the psychological dimensions.
D. Forming a partnership between the patient and the consultant.
E. Forming a partnership between the consultant and other medical specialists.

This chapter also corresponds to Chapter 30 in the *Essentials of Consultation-Liaison Psychiatry*.

40.3   Which of the following medications is an inducer of metabolism?
        A. Valproic acid.
        B. Paroxetine.
        C. Hydrazine.
        D. Isoniazid.
        E. Carbamazepine.

40.4   Most psychoactive drugs are lipophilic and are absorbed preferentially
        into fatty tissue, including the brain, **EXCEPT**
        A. Fluoxetine.
        B. Buspirone.
        C. Haloperidol.
        D. Lithium.
        E. Doxepin.

40.5   A steady-state drug level is usually achieved after
        A. 1 half-life of the drug.
        B. 2–3 half-lives of the drug.
        C. 4–5 half-lives of the drug.
        D. 6–7 half-lives of the drug.
        E. 8–9 half-lives of the drug.

40.6   The pharmacodynamic effects of one drug on another include
        A. Changing its absorption.
        B. Changing its distribution.
        C. Changing its effect at the point of action.
        D. Changing its route of excretion.
        E. Changing its biotransformation.

40.7   Barring intolerable side effects, how long should an antidepressant medi-
        cation be tried at therapeutic doses before it is considered adequate?
        A. 3 weeks.
        B. 1 month.
        C. 6 weeks.
        D. 3 months.
        E. 6 months.

40.8   A severe serotonin syndrome can be caused by combining
    A. Selective serotonin reuptake inhibitors and monoamine oxidase inhibitors.
    B. Monoamine oxidase inhibitors and benzodiazepines.
    C. Selective serotonin reuptake inhibitors and neuroleptics.
    D. Lithium and psychostimulants.
    E. Neuroleptics and benzodiazepines.

40.9   The drug(s) of choice in patients with schizophrenia are
    A. Monoamine oxidase inhibitors.
    B. Neuroleptics.
    C. Lithium.
    D. Benzodiazepines.
    E. Antidepressants.

40.10 The technique of rapid neuroleptization
    A. Is effective in calming an agitated patient.
    B. Is effective in clearing psychosis.
    C. Is effective in reducing severe panic symptoms.
    D. Is effective in treating delirium.
    E. Is more effective than conservative doses and has more side effects.

40.11 The percentage of patients treated with neuroleptics who develop tardive dyskinesia is approximately
    A. Under 10%.
    B. 10%–20%.
    C. 20%–30%.
    D. 30%–40%.
    E. More than 40%.

40.12 The mechanism of action of benzodiazepines involves
    A. Blocking dopamine reuptake.
    B. Increasing dopamine release.
    C. Inducing binding of γ-aminobutyric acid (GABA).
    D. Blocking α-noradrenergic receptors.
    E. Blocking serotonin receptors.

202 Study Guide to Consultation-Liaison Psychiatry

40.13 Which of the following tricyclic antidepressants is least likely to cause the side effect of orthostatic hypotension in patients with cardiac or neurological disease?

A. Amitriptyline.
B. Doxepin.
C. Imipramine.
D. Nortriptyline.
E. Trimipramine.

40.14 Which of the following is true?

A. In patients with renal failure, protein binding is reduced because of increased albumin levels in patients with nephrotic syndrome and because unexcreted metabolites compete for protein-binding sites.
B. Hepatic insufficiency can decrease the blood levels and half-life of all drugs except lithium by several mechanisms, including decreasing phase I metabolism through cytochrome P-450 and other oxidative enzymes.
C. Trazodone does not suppress respiration.
D. All of the above.
E. None of the above.

40.15 Which of the following is false?

A. Patients with delirium or dementia are particularly sensitive to anticholinergic effects.
B. Hypothyroidism is a contraindication to therapy with lithium.
C. Psychostimulants are preferable to neuroleptics in patients with acute traumatic brain injuries.
D. All of the above.
E. None of the above.

Directions: For each of the statements below, one or more of the answers is correct. Choose

A. If 1, 2, and 3 are correct.
B. If only 1 and 3 are correct.
C. If only 2 and 4 are correct.
D. If only 4 is correct.
E. If all are correct.

40.16 Tricyclic antidepressants are metabolized by which of the following cytochrome P-450 enzymes?
1. CYP2D6.
2. CYP3A.
3. CYP2C.
4. CYP1A2.

40.17 Which of the following can increase the sedative effects of neuroleptics?
1. Narcotics.
2. Tricyclic antidepressants.
3. Barbiturates.
4. Psychostimulants.

40.18 The most common cause(s) for low drug levels is
1. Noncompliance.
2. Receptor site activity.
3. Pharmacokinetic variables.
4. Drug interactions.

40.19 Denervation sensitivity involves
1. An increased number of receptors.
2. An increased sensitivity to the antagonist.
3. An increased sensitivity to the agonist.
4. An increased amount of ligands.

40.20 In addition to major depression, antidepressant medications can be used for
1. Eating disorders.
2. Chronic pain.
3. Anxiety disorders.
4. Incontinence.

40.21 Which of the following is a secondary tricyclic antidepressant?
1. Doxepin.
2. Amitriptyline.
3. Imipramine.
4. Desipramine.

40.22 The most frequent side effects of selective serotonin reuptake inhibitors include
1. Weight gain.
2. Nausea.
3. Sedation.
4. Headache.

40.23 Combining tricyclic antidepressants with benzodiazepines can result in
1. Increased hypotensive effects.
2. Arrhythmias.
3. Increased anticholinergic effects.
4. Increased sedation.

40.24 First-line treatments for mood stabilization in patients with primary bipolar depression include
1. Clonazepam.
2. Carbamazepine.
3. Diltiazem.
4. Lithium.

40.25 The most frequent early side effects of lithium include
1. Gastric irritation.
2. Polyuria.
3. Diarrhea.
4. Muscle fasciculation.

40.26 Long-acting benzodiazepines with a rapid onset of action include
1. Clorazepate.
2. Midazolam.
3. Diazepam.
4. Triazolam.

40.27 Advantages of buspirone in the consultation-liaison setting include that
1. It does not cause sedation.
2. It does not change the seizure threshold.
3. It does not cause functional impairment.
4. It does not have abuse potential.

40.28   Mechanisms of action through which hepatic insufficiency can increase
        blood levels and a drug's half-life include
        1.   Decreasing volume of distribution in patients with ascites.
        2.   Increasing phase I metabolism.
        3.   Decreasing free-drug levels.
        4.   Reducing phase II pathways for drugs that predominantly undergo
             glucuronidation.

40.29   Typical anticholinergic side effects include
        1.   Dry mouth.
        2.   Diarrhea.
        3.   Blurred vision.
        4.   Decreased libido.

ANSWERS*

40.1   The answer is **C.** To avoid a frightening dystonic reaction after the intro-
        duction of an antipsychotic medication for an anxious patient who is expe-
        riencing an initial episode of schizophrenia, prophylactic treatment with
        benztropine is recommended. **(p. 961)**

40.2   The answer is **B.** The term *bimodal relatedness* refers to interacting with a
        patient taking into account both the physicochemical system and the
        psychosocial dimension. **(p. 961)**

40.3   The answer is **E.** Carbamazepine is an inducer of metabolism. **(p. 962)**

40.4   The answer is **D.** Most psychoactive drugs are lipophilic and are absorbed
        preferentially into fatty tissue, including the brain, except lithium. **(p. 962)**

40.5   The answer is **C.** A steady-state drug level is usually achieved after 4–5
        half-lives of the drug. **(p. 964)**

40.6   The answer is **C.** The pharmacodynamic effects of one drug on another in-
        clude changing its effect at the point of action. **(p. 966)**

---

*Page numbers within answer sections refer to *The American Psychiatric Press Textbook
of Consultation-Liaison Psychiatry*.

40.7   The answer is **C.** Barring intolerable side effects, an antidepressant medication should be tried at therapeutic doses for 6 weeks before it is considered adequate. **(p. 967)**

40.8   The answer is **A.** A severe serotonin syndrome can be caused by combining selective serotonin reuptake inhibitors and monoamine oxidase inhibitors. **(p. 974)**

40.9   The answer is **B.** The drug(s) of choice in patients with schizophrenia are neuroleptics. **(p. 982)**

40.10   The answer is **E.** Patients treated with the technique of rapid neuroleptization have greater benefit than those treated with more conservative doses; in addition, these patients are at greater risk for side effects. **(pp. 984–985)**

40.11   The answer is **C.** The percentage of patients treated with neuroleptics who develop tardive dyskinesia is approximately 20%–30%. **(p. 986)**

40.12   The answer is **C.** The mechanism of action of benzodiazepines involves inducing binding of γ-aminobutyric acid (GABA). **(p. 990)**

40.13   The answer is **D.** Nortriptyline is the tricyclic antidepressant that is least likely to cause orthostatic hypotension in patients with cardiac or neurological disease. **(p. 996)**

40.14   The answer is **C.** Trazodone does not suppress respiration. **(p. 998)**
The other answers are false; correct answers are as follows:
In patients with renal failure, protein binding is reduced because of decreased albumin levels in patients with nephrotic syndrome and because unexcreted metabolites compete for protein-binding sites. **(p. 998)**
Hepatic insufficiency can increase the blood levels and half-life of all drugs except lithium by several mechanisms, including decreasing phase I metabolism through cytochrome P-450 and other oxidative enzymes. **(p. 998)**

40.15   The answer is **B.** Hypothyroidism is not a contraindication to therapy with lithium. **(p. 999)**

40.16   The answer is **E.** Tricyclic antidepressants are metabolized by CYP2D6, CYP3A, CYP2C, and CYP1A2. **(p. 965)**

40.17 The answer is **A.** Narcotics, tricyclic antidepressants, and barbiturates can increase the sedative effects of neuroleptics. **(p. 964)**

40.18 The answer is **B.** The most common causes for low drug levels are non-compliance and pharmacokinetic variables. **(p. 965)**

40.19 The answer is **B.** Denervation sensitivity involves an increased number of receptors and an increased sensitivity to the agonist. **(p. 966)**

40.20 The answer is **E.** In addition to major depression, antidepressant medications can be used for eating disorders, chronic pain, anxiety disorders, and incontinence. **(p. 967)**

40.21 The answer is **D.** Desipramine is a secondary tricyclic antidepressant. **(p. 968)**

40.22 The answer is **C.** The most frequent side effects of selective serotonin reuptake inhibitors include nausea and headache. **(p. 971)**

40.23 The answer is **D.** Combining tricyclic antidepressants with benzodiazepines can result in increased sedation. **(p. 973)**

40.24 The answer is **C.** First-line treatments for mood stabilization in patients with primary bipolar depression include carbamazepine and lithium. **(p. 977)**

40.25 The answer is **A.** The most frequent early side effects of lithium include gastric irritation, polyuria, and diarrhea. **(pp. 978–979)**

40.26 The answer is **B.** Long-acting benzodiazepines with a rapid onset of action include clorazepate and diazepam. **(p. 991)**

40.27 The answer is **E.** Buspirone is advantageous in the consultation-liaison setting because it does not cause sedation, does not change the seizure threshold, does not cause functional impairment, and does not have abuse potential. **(p. 993)**

40.28   The answer is **D.** Mechanisms of action through which hepatic insufficiency can increase blood levels and a drug's half-life include reducing
phase II pathways for drugs that predominantly undergo glucuronidation.
(p. 998)

40.29   The answer is **B.** Typical anticholinergic side effects include dry mouth and
blurred vision. **(p. 1000)**

Chapter 41

Chronic Pain: Neuropsychopharmacology and Adjunctive Psychiatric Treatment

QUESTIONS

Directions: Select the single best response for each of the following questions:

41.1   Allachesthesia refers to
A.   Pain caused by a noxious peripheral stimulus.
B.   Pain caused by a nonnoxious stimulus.
C.   A condition in which a sensation is referred to a site distant from which the stimulus is applied.
D.   Decreased sensitivity to any stimulation.
E.   A burning pain with allodynia.

41.2   Increased sensitivity to noxious stimulation is called
A.   Hyperesthesia.
B.   Hyperalgesia.
C.   Hyperpathia.
D.   Hypoalgesia.
E.   Allodynia.

41.3   The approximate percentage of people with chronic pain who have a psychiatric disorder is
A.   Less than 10%.
B.   10%–20%.
C.   20%–30%.
D.   30%–40%.
E.   More than 40%.

This chapter also corresponds to Chapter 31 in the *Essentials of Consultation-Liaison Psychiatry*.

41.4 Sympathetically maintained pain is usually manifested by mechanically induced
  A. Hyperesthesia.
  B. Hyperalgesia.
  C. Hyperpathia.
  D. Hypoalgesia.
  E. Allodynia.

41.5 Which of the following is false?
  A. Patients with pain have about the same prevalence of psychiatric diagnoses as do other medically ill populations.
  B. The most common comorbid conditions with somatoform disorders are major depression and anxiety disorder.
  C. Borderline personality disorder is present in a majority of chronic pain patients.
  D. All of the above.
  E. None of the above.

41.6 Which of the following can be used to prevent nonsteroidal anti-inflammatory drug (NSAID)–induced gastric ulcers?
  A. Ketorolac.
  B. Oxaprozin.
  C. Etodolac.
  D. Misoprostol.
  E. All of the above.

41.7 Which of the following is true?
  A. Antihistamines can have an analgesic effect.
  B. Carbamazepine is generally superior to phenytoin for relief of pain.
  C. The ischemic arm block is one of the most useful methods for treating sympathetically maintained pain.
  D. All of the above.
  E. None of the above.

41.8 Substance P enhances pain transmission through the spinal cord by activation of
  A. Somatostatin.
  B. γ-Aminobutyric acid (GABA).
  C. *N*-methyl-D-aspartate (NMDA).
  D. Calcitonin.
  E. Norepinephrine.

Directions: For each of the statements below, one or more of the answers is correct. Choose

    A. If 1, 2, and 3 are correct.
    B. If only 1 and 3 are correct.
    C. If only 2 and 4 are correct.
    D. If only 4 is correct.
    E. If all are correct.

41.9   Pain is an illness for patients with the following:
    1. Reflex sympathetic dystrophy.
    2. Trauma.
    3. Anesthesia dolorosa.
    4. Sickle cell crises.

41.10   Preventing the sensitization of wide dynamic range cells in reflex sympathetic dystrophy syndromes may involve
    1. Early physical therapy.
    2. α-Blockade.
    3. Treatment of acute pain.
    4. Substance P antagonists.

41.11   *N*-methyl-D-aspartate (NMDA) receptors are stimulated by
    1. Myofascial trigger points.
    2. Acute pain.
    3. Neurotoxins.
    4. Chronic pain.

41.12   Hyperalgesia can be reversed by
    1. γ-Aminobutyric acid (GABA) antagonists.
    2. Opiates.
    3. Substance P antagonists.
    4. *N*-methyl-D-aspartate (NMDA) antagonists.

41.13   Frequent muscle trigger points for fibromyalgia include
    1. Temporalis.
    2. Sternocleidomastoid.
    3. Rhomboids.
    4. Longissimus thoracis.

41.14 Diagnosis of a depressed patient with chronic pain can be accomplished with the aid of
       1. The Minnesota Multiphasic Personality Inventory (MMPI).
       2. A visual analogue scale.
       3. A sleep electroencephalogram (EEG).
       4. CAGE questionnaire.

41.15 The potential pain-relieving effects of antidepressants include
       1. Antihistamine effects.
       2. Local anesthetic membrane-stabilizing effects.
       3. Peptide synergy.
       4. Binding to brain opiate receptors.

41.16 Which of the following are effective pain adjuvants?
       1. Methylphenidate.
       2. Alcohol.
       3. Amphetamine.
       4. Flupentixol.

ANSWERS*

41.1   The answer is **C.** Allachesthesia refers to a condition in which a sensation is referred to a site distant from which the stimulus is applied. **(p. 1007)**

41.2   The answer is **B.** Increased sensitivity to noxious stimulation is called hyperalgesia. **(p. 1007)**

41.3   The answer is **C.** The approximate percentage of people with chronic pain who have a psychiatric disorder is 20%–30%. **(p. 1009)**

41.4   The answer is **E.** Sympathetically maintained pain is usually manifested by mechanically induced allodynia. **(p. 1011)**

41.5   The answer is **D.** No single personality type or pathology is uniquely associated with chronic pain. **(p. 1019)**

---

*Page numbers within answer sections refer to *The American Psychiatric Press Textbook of Consultation-Liaison Psychiatry*.

41.6   The answer is **D.** Misoprostol can be used to prevent nonsteroidal antiinflammatory drug–induced gastric ulcers. **(p. 1022)**

41.7   The answer is **D.** All of the statements are true. Antihistamines can have an analgesic effect. Carbamazepine is generally superior to phenytoin for relief of pain. The ischemic arm block is one of the most useful methods for treating sympathetically maintained pain. **(pp. 1025–1026)**

41.8   The answer is **C.** Substance P enhances pain transmission through the spinal cord by activation of N-methyl-D-aspartate. **(p. 1027)**

41.9   The answer is **B.** Pain is an illness for patients with reflex sympathetic dystrophy and anesthesia dolorosa. **(p. 1007)**

41.10   The answer is **A.** Preventing the sensitization of wide dynamic range cells in reflex sympathetic dystrophy syndromes may involve early physical therapy, α-blockade, and treatment of acute pain. **(p. 1010)**

41.11   The answer is **D.** N-methyl-D-aspartate receptors are stimulated by chronic pain. **(p. 1010)**

41.12   The answer is **C.** Hyperalgesia can be reversed by opiates and N-methyl-D-aspartate antagonists. **(p. 1010)**

41.13   The answer is **E.** Frequent muscle trigger points for fibromyalgia include the temporalis, sternocleidomastoid, rhomboids, and longissimus thoracis. **(p. 1011)**

41.14   The answer is **A.** Diagnosis of a depressed patient with chronic pain can be accomplished with the aid of the Minnesota Multiphasic Personality Inventory (MMPI), a visual analogue scale, and a sleep electroencephalogram. **(p. 1014)**

41.15   The answer is **E.** The potential pain-relieving effects of antidepressants include antihistamine effects, local anesthetic membrane-stabilizing effects, peptide synergy, and binding to brain opiate receptors. **(p. 1027)**

41.16   The answer is **B.** Methylphenidate and amphetamine are effective pain adjuvants. **(p. 1028)**

Chapter 42

Electroconvulsive Therapy: An Overview

Directions: Select the single best response for each of the following questions:

42.1 Electroconvulsive therapy (ECT) treatments are usually given
   A. Once a week for 2–4 weeks.
   B. Once a week for 6–12 weeks.
   C. Twice a week for 2–4 weeks.
   D. Three times per week for 2–4 weeks.
   E. Four times per week for 2–4 weeks.

42.2 The most commonly observed side effect of electroconvulsive therapy (ECT) is
   A. Seizures.
   B. Cardiac arrhythmias.
   C. Extensive memory loss.
   D. Transient cognitive impairment.
   E. Myalgias.

42.3 The efficacy of electroconvulsive therapy (ECT) in Parkinson's disease is probably due to
   A. Electroconvulsive therapy's (ECT's) dopamine-enhancing effect.
   B. Increased cerebral blood flow.
   C. Increased intracranial pressure.
   D. Endorphin release.
   E. Immune system enhancement.

This chapter also corresponds to Chapter 32 in the *Essentials of Consultation-Liaison Psychiatry*.

42.4   Which of the following is true?
   A.   Epileptic patients should discontinue anticonvulsant medications dur-
        ing a course of electroconvulsive therapy (ECT).
   B.   Regularly prescribed cardiac medications should be given to patients
        with ischemic heart disease prior to each electroconvulsive therapy
        (ECT) treatment.
   C.   Patients with cardiac pacemakers are contraindicated for electro-
        convulsive therapy (ECT).
   D.   All of the above.
   E.   None of the above.

42.5   Which of the following is false?
   A.   Increasing age is associated with a favorable response to
        electroconvulsive therapy (ECT).
   B.   Electroconvulsive therapy (ECT) may be preferred over psychotropic
        medications during pregnancy.
   C.   Patients with intracranial tumors should not receive electroconvulsive
        therapy (ECT).
   D.   All of the above.
   E.   None of the above.

Directions: For each of the statements below, one or more of the answers is
correct. Choose

   A.   If 1, 2, and 3 are correct.
   B.   If only 1 and 3 are correct.
   C.   If only 2 and 4 are correct.
   D.   If only 4 is correct.
   E.   If all are correct.

42.6   Indications for electroconvulsive therapy (ECT) include
   1.   Major depressive episode.
   2.   Schizoaffective disorder.
   3.   Catatonia.
   4.   Panic disorder.

42.7   Electroconvulsive therapy (ECT) is used as a first-line treatment when
   1.   There is a need for rapid improvement.
   2.   The patient's family prefers electroconvulsive therapy (ECT).
   3.   Other treatments are considered more risky.
   4.   Depression is unipolar.

42.8   Common medical conditions that increase the risk of adverse events during electroconvulsive therapy (ECT) include
    1.   Chronic obstructive pulmonary disease.
    2.   Hypertension.
    3.   Asthma.
    4.   Cardiac arrhythmia.

ANSWERS*

42.1   The answer is **D.** Electroconvulsive therapy treatments are usually given three times per week for 2–4 weeks. **(p. 1042)**

42.2   The answer is **D.** The most commonly observed side effect of electroconvulsive therapy is transient cognitive impairment. **(p. 1043)**

42.3   The answer is **A.** The efficacy of electroconvulsive therapy in Parkinson's disease is probably due to electroconvulsive therapy's dopamine-enhancing effect. **(p. 1043)**

42.4   The answer is **B.** Regularly prescribed cardiac medications should be given to patients with ischemic heart disease prior to each electroconvulsive therapy treatment. **(p. 1045)**
The other answers are false; correct answers are as follows:
Epileptic patients should continue to receive their anticonvulsant medications during a course of electroconvulsive therapy. **(p. 1045)**
Patients with cardiac pacemakers can safely receive electroconvulsive therapy. **(p. 1046)**

42.5   The answer is **C.** Patients with intracranial tumors can receive electroconvulsive therapy after careful consideration of the risk-benefit ratio. **(p. 1046)**

42.6   The answer is **A.** Indications for electroconvulsive therapy include major depressive episode, schizoaffective disorder, and catatonia. **(p. 1039)**

*Page numbers within answer sections refer to *The American Psychiatric Press Textbook of Consultation-Liaison Psychiatry.*

42.7   The answer is **B.** Electroconvulsive therapy is used as a first-line treatment when there is a need for rapid improvement and when other treatments are considered more risky. **(pp. 1039–1040)**

42.8   The answer is **E.** Common medical conditions that increase the risk of adverse events during electroconvulsive therapy include chronic obstructive pulmonary disease, hypertension, asthma, and cardiac arrhythmia. **(p. 1040)**

Chapter 43

Psychotherapy

 QUESTIONS

Directions: Select the single best response for each of the following questions:

43.1 The five major psychotherapeutic principles include all of the following **EXCEPT**
   A. Suggestion.
   B. Abreaction.
   C. Transference.
   D. Manipulation.
   E. Clarification.

43.2 In psychotherapeutic practice, attempting to change the patient's attitudes by explaining unconscious thoughts is known as
   A. Intervention.
   B. Interpretation.
   C. Abreaction.
   D. Clarification.
   E. Countertransference.

43.3 A woman with breast cancer who has found it difficult to speak about her illness would be most likely to benefit from which of the following psychotherapeutic formats?
   A. Couples therapy.
   B. Group therapy.
   C. Reconstructive therapy.
   D. Extensive therapy.
   E. Reeducational therapy.

This chapter also corresponds to Chapter 33 in the *Essentials of Consultation-Liaison Psychiatry.*

43.4   Which of the following treatment approaches would be most appropriate
        for a patient with a dramatizing, histrionic personality type?
        A. A calm, professional approach.
        B. A scientific approach.
        C. A limit-setting approach.
        D. A challenging approach.
        E. A life narrative approach.

43.5   The consultant can obtain both psychological and physiological informa-
        tion about a patient's symptoms through the technique known as
        A. Debriefing.
        B. Personality diagnosis.
        C. Therapeutic alliance.
        D. Associative anamnesis.
        E. Medical hypnosis.

43.6   An outpatient with a chronic medical illness who uses somatization as a
        major defense could benefit from
        A. Supportive psychotherapy.
        B. Exploratory psychotherapy.
        C. Therapeutic alliance.
        D. Electroconvulsive therapy (ECT).
        E. Brief, intermittent, attenuated therapy.

Directions: For each of the statements below, one or more of the answers is
correct. Choose

        A. If 1, 2, and 3 are correct.
        B. If only 1 and 3 are correct.
        C. If only 2 and 4 are correct.
        D. If only 4 is correct.
        E. If all are correct.

43.7   Compared with psychoanalysis, psychodynamic psychotherapy is more
        focused on
        1. Symptomatic relief.
        2. The therapeutic relationship.
        3. Environmental circumstances.
        4. Intrapsychic conflicts.

43.8 Psychotherapeutic intervention in a general medical hospital differs from traditional psychiatric practice in the following ways:
  1. Patients have greater motivation and receptivity.
  2. There is a lack of privacy.
  3. Use of exploratory techniques is greater.
  4. Encounters are briefer.

43.9 An exploratory therapeutic approach is most appropriate for patients who
  1. Have a high level of cognitive functioning.
  2. Are hospital inpatients.
  3. Have a high level of motivation to change.
  4. Have a poor external support system.

ANSWERS*

43.1 The answer is **C.** The five major psychotherapeutic principles are suggestion, abreaction, manipulation, clarification, and interpretation. **(p. 1055)**

43.2 The answer is **B.** In psychotherapeutic practice, attempting to change the patient's attitudes by explaining unconscious thoughts is known as interpretation. **(p. 1057)**

43.3 The answer is **B.** A woman with breast cancer who has found it difficult to speak about her illness would be most likely to benefit from group therapy. **(p. 1058)**

43.4 The answer is **A.** A calm, professional approach is most appropriate for a patient with a dramatizing, histrionic personality type. **(p. 1063)**

43.5 The answer is **D.** The consultant can obtain both psychological and physiological information about a patient's symptoms through the technique of associative anamnesis. **(p. 1065)**

43.6 The answer is **E.** An outpatient with a chronic medical illness who uses somatization as a major defense could benefit from brief, intermittent, attenuated therapy. **(p. 1073)**

---

*Page numbers within answer sections refer to *The American Psychiatric Press Textbook of Consultation-Liaison Psychiatry.*

43.7   The answer is **A.** Compared with psychoanalysis, psychodynamic psycho-
        therapy is more focused on symptomatic relief, the therapeutic relation-
        ship, and environmental circumstances. **(p. 1056)**

43.8   The answer is **C.** Psychotherapeutic intervention in a general medical hos-
        pital differs from traditional psychiatric practice in that there is a lack of pri-
        vacy and encounters tend to be more brief. **(pp. 1057–1059)**

43.9   The answer is **B.** An exploratory therapeutic approach is most appropriate
        for patients who have a high level of cognitive functioning and a high level
        of motivation to change. **(p. 1069)**

Chapter 44

Behavioral Medicine

Directions: Select the single best response for each of the following questions:

44.1   Which of the following is true?
   A.   Adherence to treatment is lower in patients with ischemic heart disease who have depressive symptoms.
   B.   Patients with major depressive disorder have a higher mortality from ischemic heart disease.
   C.   Psychobehavioral pathways are mediated by the impact of exogenous substances such as alcohol.
   D.   All of the above.
   E.   None of the above.

44.2   Which of the following is false?
   A.   Type A behavior is predictive of ischemic heart disease risk.
   B.   Benzodiazepines are effective in reducing hostility.
   C.   If a patient with a history of depression quits smoking, the risk of recurrence of depressive symptoms is reduced.
   D.   All of the above.
   E.   None of the above.

This chapter also corresponds to Chapter 34 in the *Essentials of Consultation-Liaison Psychiatry.*

223

44.3   The single best predictor of actual job loss for patients with ischemic heart
        disease 1 year after initial evaluation is
        A.   Number of myocardial infarctions.
        B.   Level of depression.
        C.   Educational level.
        D.   Sexual activity.
        E.   Participation in psychotherapy.

44.4   The term *syndrome X* refers to unexplained
        A.   Panic symptoms.
        B.   Chronic constipation.
        C.   Chest pain or discomfort.
        D.   Ulcer disease.
        E.   Any form of unidentifiable pain.

44.5   The study of how behavior and mental states affect immune function is
        known as
        A.   Psychosomatic medicine.
        B.   Psychoneuroimmunology.
        C.   Psychophysiology.
        D.   Psyche-soma relationship.
        E.   All of the above.

44.6   The MADISON scale is used for patients with
        A.   Hyperimmune disorders.
        B.   Autoimmune disorders.
        C.   Chronic pain.
        D.   Cancer.
        E.   Sexual dysfunction.

Directions: For each of the statements below, one or more of the answers is
correct. Choose

        A.   If 1, 2, and 3 are correct.
        B.   If only 1 and 3 are correct.
        C.   If only 2 and 4 are correct.
        D.   If only 4 is correct.
        E.   If all are correct.

44.7   Associations between hostility and ischemic heart disease include
        1. Sudden death by ventricular arrhythmia.
        2. Increased atherosclerosis.
        3. Precipitation of myocardial ischemia.
        4. Persistent smoking after diagnosis of heart disease.

44.8   The physiological and psychological benefits of exercise include
        1. Increase in muscle mass.
        2. Improved glucose tolerance.
        3. Increase in peak oxygen intake.
        4. Decreased need for sleep.

44.9   Characteristics found in patients with chronic pelvic pain include
        1. Vocational dysfunction.
        2. Emotional distress.
        3. Medical disability.
        4. History of sexual abuse.

ANSWERS*

44.1   The answer is **D.** All of the answers are true. Adherence to treatment is
        lower in patients with ischemic heart disease who have depressive symp-
        toms. Patients with major depressive disorder have a higher mortality from
        ischemic heart disease. Psychobehavioral pathways are mediated by the
        impact of exogenous substances such as alcohol. **(pp. 1082–1083)**

44.2   The answer is **D.** All of the answers are false; correct answers are as fol-
        lows:
        Hostility, but not Type A behavior, is predictive of ischemic heart disease
        risk. **(p. 1083)**
        Benzodiazepines do not alter hostility. **(p. 1086)**
        If a patient with a history of depression quits smoking, depressive symp-
        toms may recur. **(p. 1089)**

44.3   The answer is **B.** The single best predictor of actual job loss for patients
        with ischemic heart disease 1 year after initial evaluation is level of depres-
        sion. **(p. 1090)**

---

*Page numbers within answer sections refer to *The American Psychiatric Press Textbook
of Consultation-Liaison Psychiatry.*

44.4   The answer is **C.** The term *syndrome X* refers to chest pain or discomfort. **(p. 1090)**

44.5   The answer is **B.** The study of how behavior and mental states affect immune function is known as psychoneuroimmunology. **(p. 1092)**

44.6   The answer is **C.** The MADISON scale is used for patients with chronic pain. **(p. 1097)**

44.7   The answer is **E.** Associations between hostility and ischemic heart disease include sudden death by ventricular arrhythmia, increased atherosclerosis, precipitation of myocardial ischemia, and persistent smoking after diagnosis of heart disease. **(p. 1083)**

44.8   The answer is **A.** The physiological and psychological benefits of exercise include increase in muscle mass, improved glucose tolerance, and increase in peak oxygen intake. **(p. 1087)**

44.9   The answer is **E.** Characteristics found in patients with chronic pelvic pain include vocational dysfunction, emotional distress, medical disability, and a history of sexual abuse. **(p. 1099)**